Lotus Illustrated DICTIONARY of

ELECTRICAL ENGINEERING

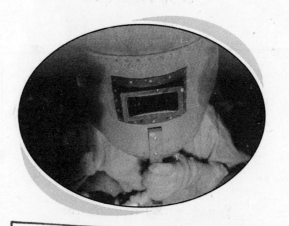

Lotus PRESS
4263 / 3, Ansari Road,
Daryaganj, New Delhi-02

lotus *Illustrated*

DICTIONARY
of

ELECTRICAL
ENGINEERING

ISBN 81 89093 30 4

Published by:
LOTUS PRESS
4263/3, Ansari Road, Daryaganj,
New Delhi-110002
Ph: 32903912, 23280047
E-mail: lotus_press@sify.com
www: lotuspress.co.in

Printed at: **Saras Graphics**, Delhi

PREFACE

This dictionary of Electrical Engineering is meant for all those people who are in search of excellent, real and relevant material on the subject. The matter included in the dictionary is well-researched one, precise and presented in such a comprehensive and simple language such that even a novice can understand the point behind it. This dictionary contains all terms with exhaustive definitions. Many of the terms are supplemented by their pictorial representations. The pictorial representations help the readers to grasp the core behind the term. These representations not just elaborate the definition but provide supplementary knowledge associated with the term. Many of the terms included are rare and hard to find in any of the contemporary books. With so much advancement in the field of Electrical Engineering, the emerging situation demands to include all the recent happenings. With the introduction of computers, the field of Electrical Engineering has taken a sharp rise. All the latest material is being included which will certainly give a boost to the reader who are in search of something new. This dictionary contains the terms from all the branches with proportionate weightage to each branch related to Electrical Engineering.

This dictionary will certainly prove to be a boon for all the readers of the subject.

■ 1xN

this term is a type of switching configuration. It has a single input that can be connected to multiple outputs (N), or the opposite (many inputs that could be connected to a single output). This is a simple way to describe a matrix (or MxN) with one axis having a single port.

■ 3-way

3-way dimming control allows dimming or switching from one location (using a 3-way dimmer) and on/off switching from a second location (using a 3-way switch).

■ 4-way

4-way dimming control allows dimming from one location only (using a 3-way dimmer) and on/off switching from two or more additional locations (using a combination of 3-way and 4-way switches).

■ abnormal failure

an artificially induced failure of a component, usually as a result of 'abnormals' testing for regulatory agency safety compliance.

■ absolute maximum ratings

specifications that, if exceeded, could cause permanent damage to the converter. There are not continuous ratings, and proper operation is not implied.

■ absolute measuring system

the measuring value is determined by reading information from a scale, without counting. The measuring value is immediately available after switch-on.

■ absolute permeability

the permeability of a magnetic material expressed in actual physical units, not relative to permeability of free space. The permeability of magnetic materials is rarely expressed in terms of absolute permeability. The usual mode is in terms of relative permeability.

■ absolute pressure

gauge pressure plus atmospheric pressure.

■ absolute pressure transducer

a transducer which measures pressure in relation to zero pressure (a vacuum on one side of the diaphragm).

■ absolute zero

temperature at which thermal energy is at a minimum. Defined as 0 Kelvin, calculated to be -273.15°C or -459.67°F.

■ absorption (fiber optic)

one cause of fiber optic attenuation where light signal is absorbed into the glass during transmission.

■ AC

alternating Current; an electric current that reverses its direction at regularly recurring intervals.

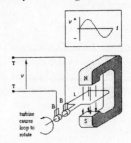

turbine causes loop to rotate

■ AC filter

a filter circuit that removes unwanted frequencies (harmonics) from a mostly AC current.
This would include some EMI
filters.

■ AC flux density (gauss)

number of flux lines per unit of
cross-sectional area generated by
an alternating magnetic field.

■ ac motors

a motor (see motor definition)
operating on AC current that
flows in either direction (AC current). There are two general
types: <u>Induction</u>, and <u>Synchro-
nous</u>.

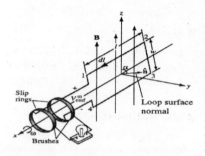

■ acceleration

a change in the velocity of a body
or particle with respect to time.
The parameter that an accelerometer measures (dv/dt). Units expressed in "g".

■ accelerometer

a device which converts the effects of mechanical motion
into an electrical signal that is
proportional to the acceleration value of the motion. A
sensor.

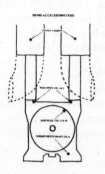

■ acceptor

a type of impurity that accepts or
takes electrons from the atoms of
a semiconductor.

■ access method

the method by which networked
stations determine when they can
transmit data on a shared transmission medium. Also, the software within an SNA processor that
controls the flow of information
through a network.

■ access provider

organisation providing and main-
taining network services for subscribers.

■ access rate

the transmission speed, in bits per
second, of the physical access circuit between the end user and the
network.

■ accessible

1. (as applied to wiring methods)
capable of being removed or exposed without damaging the building structure or finish, or not permanently closed in by the structure or finish of the building.
2. (as applied to equipment) Ad-

mitting close approach: not guarded by locked doors, elevation, or other effective means. (see **accessible, readily**)

■ **accessible, readily**

(Readily Accessible) capable of being reached quickly for operation, renewal, or inspections, without requiring those to whom ready access is requisite to climb over or remove obstacles or to resort to portable ladders, chairs etc.

■ **accuracy**

the closeness of an indication or reading of a measurement device to the actual value of the quantity being measured. Usually expressed as ± percent of full scale output or reading.

■ **accuracy grade**

grade of quality, determined by the max. permissible measuring deviations within a predetermined measuring range (e.g. 1m)

■ **acoustics**

the degree of sound. The nature, cause, and phenomena of the vibrations of elastic bodies; which vibrations create compressional waves or wave fronts which are transmitted through various media, such as air, water, wood, steel, etc.

■ **active high**

power switch enable input voltage must exceed the devices defined threshold voltage for the device to turn on (typically 1.5V). Conversely, enable input voltage must fall below the threshold voltage to turn the device off.

■ **active iron**

the amount of steel (iron) in the stator and rotor of a motor. Usually the amount of active iron is increased or decreased by lengthening or shortening the rotor and stator (they are generally the same length).

■ **active low**

power switch enable input voltage must fall below the devices defined threshold voltage for the device to turn on (typically 1.5V). Conversely, enable input voltage must exceed the threshold voltage to turn the device off.

■ **active video**

the portion of a video signal that contains the visible picture information.

■ **activity**

a thermodynamic term for the apparent or active concentration of a free ion in solution. It is related to concentration by the activity coefficient.

■ **activity coefficient**

a ratio of the activity of species I to its molality (C). It is a correction factor which makes the thermodynamic calculations correct. This factor is dependent on ionic strength, temperature, and other parameters. Individual ionic activity coefficients, f+ for cation and f- for an anion, cannot be derived thermodynamically. They can be calculated only by using the Debye-Huckel law for low concentration solutions in which the interionic forces depend primarily on charge, radius, and distribution of the ions and on the dielectric constant of the medium rather than on the chemical properties of the ions. Mean ionic activity coefficient (f±) or the activity of a salt, on the other hand, can be measured by a variety of techniques such as freezing point depression and vapor pressure as well as paired sensing electrodes. It is the geometric mean of the individual ionic activity coefficients: $f\pm = (f+n+f-n-)1/n$

■ activity dip

a term used to describe a sudden increase followed by a return to the previous level of the activity of a crystal unit.

■ actuator

a power conversion device (e.g. pneumatic motor, pneumatic valve, hydraulic motor, electric motor, etc.) which is responsible for generating control signals to the plant.

■ adapter

a mechanism or device for attaching non-mating parts.

■ ADC

analog-to-Digital Converter: an electronic device which converts analog signals to an equivalent digital form, in either a binary code or a binary-coded-decimal code. When used for dynamic waveforms, the sampling rate must be high to prevent aliasing errors from occurring.

■ address

The label or number identifying the memory location where a unit of information is stored.

■ adjuncation

rummage party.

■ ASDL

a new method of transmitting at speeds up to 7 Mbps in one direction over a single copper telephone line, with up to 640 kbps in the other direction.

■ afv/audio-follow-video

a control mode in a routing switcher (switching array) in which the audio inputs associated with a video input are automatically selected when the video source is selected. That is, audio and video are always switched together. See **breakaway**. Audio may be either single channel or multichannel (stereo).

■ aging

operating a converter under controlled conditions for a predetermined time in order to screen out failures. Also see **burn-in**.

■ air core inductance

the inductance that would be measured if the core had unity permeability and the flux distribution remained unaltered. (A measure of the inductance of a coil without a core.)

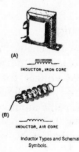

(A)
INDUCTOR, IRON CORE

(B)
INDUCTOR, AIR CORE

Inductor Types and Schematic Symbols.

■ air gap

1. a non-magnetic discontinuity in a ferro-magnetic circuit. For example, the space between the poles of a magnet, if filled with brass, wood, or any other non-magnetic material, is nevertheless called an air gap. Air gaps are often introduced into soft ferrite cores to prevent saturation at high DC bias currents or to simply hold a tight inductance tolerance.
2. the space between the rotating (rotor) and stationary (stator) member in an electric motor.

■ air pressure switch

used on motors with blowers to measure the difference in pressure across the filter so as to detect a clogged filter.

■ air temperature switch

a device used in air hooded motors to detect the temperature of the exhausted air. When used in this manner an air temperature switch will detect blockage in the cooling air system or long-term motor overload.

■ air-gap switch

a mechanical switch or relay that disconnects power to a load by physically separating two contacts, resulting in an air gap between the contacts.

■ al value (nh/n2)

the inductance rating of a core in nano Henries per turn squared (nH/N2) based on a peak flux density of 10 gauss (1 milliTesla) at a frequency of 10 kHz. An AL value of 40 would produce

400μH of inductance for 100 turns and 40mH for 1000 turns.

■ aliasing

if the sample rate of a function (fs) is less than two times the highest frequency value of the function, the frequency is ambiguously presented. The frequencies above (fs/2) will be folded back into the lower frequencies producing erroneous data.

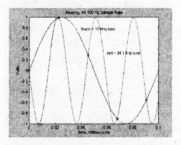

■ alloy 11

a compensating alloy used in conjunction with pure copper as the negative leg to form extension wire for platinum-platinum rhodium thermocouples Types R and S.

■ alloy 200/226

The combination of compensating alloys used with tungsten vs. tungsten 26% rhenium thermocouples as extension cable for applications under 200°C.

■ alloy 203/225

the combination of compensating alloys used with tungsten 3% rhenium vs. tungsten 150 rhenium thermocouples as extension cable for applications under 200°C.

■ alloy 405/426

the combination of compensating

alloys used with tungsten 5% rhenium vs. tungsten 26% rhenium thermocouples as extension cable for applications under 870°C.

■ ALMP

Agricultural Load Management Program.

■ alphanumeric

a character set that contains both letters and digits.

■ alternating current

an electric flow that reverses its direction at regular recurring intervals. Each forward-backward motion interval is called a cycle. Electric current in the United States alternates with a frequency of 60 hertz or cycles per second. (see **direct current**)

■ alternating voltage

a voltage which periodically changes its polarity.

■ alternation

one-half of a cycle, consisting of the complete rise and fall of an alternating voltage or current in one direction.

■ alternator

an electric generator producing an electric current that reverses its direction regularly and continually.

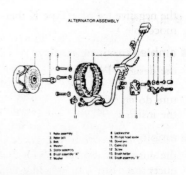

ALTERNATOR ASSEMBLY

■ altitude

the atmospheric altitude (height above sea level) at which the motor will be operating; NEMA standards call for an altitude not exceeding 3,300 ft. (1,000 meters). As the altitude increases above 3,300 ft. and the air density decreases, the air stability to cool the motor decreases - for higher altitudes higher grades of insulation or a motor derating are required. DC motors require special brushes for high altitudes.

■ ALU

Arithmetic Logic Unit. The part of a CPU where binary data is acted upon with mathematical operations.

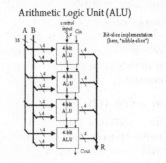

Arithmetic Logic Unit (ALU)

■ alumel

an aluminum nickel alloy used in

the negative leg of a Type K thermocouple.

■ ambient compensation

the design of an instrument such that changes in ambient temperature do not affect the readings of the instrument.

■ ambient conditions

the conditions around the transducer (pressure, temperature, etc.).

■ ambient pressure

pressure of the air surrounding a transducer.

■ ambient temperature

the temperature of the air, water, or surrounding earth. Conductor ampacity is corrected for changes in ambient temperature including temperatures below 86°F. The cooling effect can increase the current carrying capacity of the conductor.

■ american wire gauge (awg)

a U.S. standard set of non-ferrous wire conductor sizes. Typical data wiring is AWG number 24, 26 or 28. The higher the gauge number, the smaller the diameter and the thinner the wire.

■ ammeter

an electric meter used to measure current, calibrated in amperes.

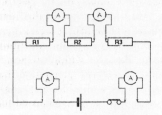

■ amorphous

refers to magnetic materials that are metallurgically non-crystalline in nature.

■ amp meter

an instrument that indicates the rate of flow of electricity through a circuit.

■ ampacity

the current-carrying capacity of conductors or equipment, expressed in amperes.

■ ampere (amp)

a unit used to define the rate of flow of electricity (current) in a circuit; units are one coulomb (6.25×10^8 electrons) per second.

■ ampere turns

the product of current (I) flowing in the winding times the number of turns (N).

■ ampere-turns per meter (at/m or a/m)

the MKS unit of magnetising force, H, as shown by Amperes Law.

■ amplifier

a device which draws power from a source other than the input signal and which produces as an output an enlarged reproduction of the essential features of its input.

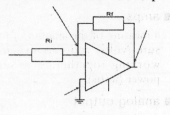

Amplifier Gain = - Rf/Ri

■ amplitude

a measurement of the distance from the highest to the lowest excursion of motion, as in the case of mechanical body in oscillation or the peak-to-peak swing of an electrical waveform.

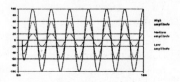

■ amplitude evaluation

method of evaluating signals generated by dynamic scanning (with carrier frequency): the amplitude variation of two alternating voltages of the same frequency are used to determine the measuring value.

■ amplitude permeability (μa)

the quotient of the peak value of flux density and peak value of applied field strength at a stated amplitude of either, with no static field present.

■ amplitude span

The Y-axis range of a graphic display of data in either the time or frequency domain. Usually a log display (dB) but can also be linear.

■ amps

a measure of the amount of pressure (volts) and current (amps) working together to produce power (watts).

■ analog output

a voltage or current signal that is a continuous function of the measured parameter.

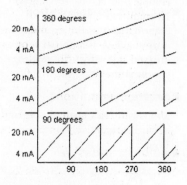

■ analog signals

signals that are continuously varying in level are said to be analog.

■ analog-to-digital (AD) converter

converts an analog signal (such as a voltage signal from a temperature sensor) into a digital signal suitable for input to a computer.

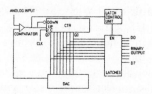

■ ancillary services market

this market is used to ensure grid reliability. It takes place a day ahead and an hour ahead of when customers actually use the electricity. Available for sale in this market are: replacement reserves (generation that can begin contributing to the grid within an hour); spinning reserves (generation that is operating, with additional capacity that can be dispatched within

10 minutes); non-spinning reserves (generation that is not operating, but can be operating within
10 minutes); and regulation (generation that is operating and whose
output can be increasased or decreased instantly to keep energy
supply and energy use in balance.)

■ anemometer

an instrument for measuring and/
or indicating the velocity of air
flow.

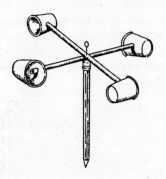

■ angle

the angle at which a resonator plate
is cut from the quartz stone in
relation to the original crystallo-
graphic axes. The angle of cut is
critical to the performance of the
crystal unit, particularly in the area
of frequency deviation over a
temperature range.

■ angle adapter

adapter base used to offset the
meter for reading purposes.

■ angle encoder

angle measuring device, converts
the shaft rotation angle into electrical signals (can be incremental
or absolute).

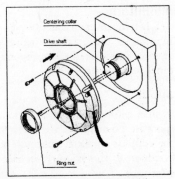

Mounting a RON angle encoder with hollow through shaft

■ angstrom

ten to the minus tenth meters.
(10^{-10}) or one millimicron, a unit
used to define the wave length of
light.

■ angular frequency

the motion of a body or a point
moving circularly, referred to as
the circular frequency O which is
the frequency in cycles per second (cps) multiplied by the term
(2) and expressed in radians per
second (2pf).

■ anion

a negatively charged ion (Cl^-,
NO^{3-}, S^{2-} etc.)

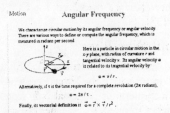

Motion　　　　Angular Frequency

We characterize circular motion by its angular frequency or angular velocity
There are various ways to define or compute the angular frequency, which is
measured in radians per second

Here is a particle in circular motion in the
x-y plane, with radius of curvature r and
tangential velocity v. Its angular velocity ω
is related to its tangential velocity by

$$\omega = v/r.$$

Alternatively, if τ is the time required for a complete revolution (2π radians),

$$\omega = 2\pi/\tau.$$

Finally, its **vectorial definition** is $\vec{\omega} = \vec{r} \times \vec{v}/r^2$.

■ anisotropic

a material whose electrical properties vary with different polariza-
tion of a travelling wave.

■ **anneal**

a high-temperature conditioning of magnetic material to relieve stresses introduced when the material was formed.

■ **anode**

1. in a diode, the electrode that must be positive with respect to the cathode to allow the diode to conduct. 2. the plate of an electron tube.

■ **ANSI**

American National Standards Institute.

■ **ANSI t1.403**

the performance-monitoring, data-link, and network interface requirements for ESF CSUs as defined by the Exchange Carriers Standards Association. T1.403 specifies automatic performance reports transmitted to the network once per second via the data link. (In an E1 environment, Performance Monitor is the equivalent of T1.403).

■ **ANSI t1.413**

the interface standard for DMT ADSL.

■ **anti-alias filter**

an anti-alias (or anti-aliasing) filter allows through the lower frequency components of a signal but stops higher frequencies, in either the signal or noise, from introducing distortion. Anti-alias filters are specified according to the sampling rate of the system and there must be one filter per input signal.

■ **anti-friction bearing**

an anti-friction bearing is a bearing utilising rolling elements between the stationary and rotating assemblies.

■ **anti-reset windup**

this is a feature in a three-mode PID controller which prevents the integral (auto reset) circuit from functioning when the temperature is outside the proportional band.

■ **apparent power**

a value of power for AC circuits that is calculated as the product of RMS current times RMS voltage, without taking the power factor into account.

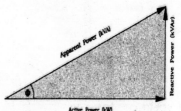

■ **application program**

a computer program that accomplishes specific tasks, such as word processing.

■ **arc**

the flow of electric current across the gap in a circuit which causes a light or a glow.

■ **argument**

input parameter to a program.

■ **armature**

the portion of the magnetic structure of a DC or universal motor which rotates

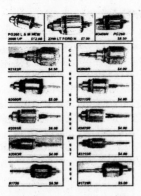

■ armature current, amps

rated full load armature circuit current.

■ armature inductance, mH

armature inductance in milli-henries (saturated).

■ armature reaction

the current that flows in the armature winding of a DC motor tends to produce magnetic flux in addition to that produced by the field current. This effect, which reduces the torque capacity, is called armature reaction and can effect the commutation and the magnitude of the motor's generated voltage.

■ armature resistance, ohms

armature resistance is measured in ohms at $25f$ C. (cold)

■ ASCII

American Standard Code for Information Interchange. A 7-bit binary code representing the English alphabet, decimal numbers and common punctuation marks. Also includes "control characters" such as Carriage Return or End of Text. An 8-bit superset of the standard ASCII codes is often used today to include foreign characters and other symbols. These supersets are often called Extended ASCII Character Sets.

■ ASIC

Application Specific Integrated Circuit

■ ASME

American Society of Mechanical Engineers.

■ ASP

Application Service Provider

■ assembler

a program that translates assembly language instructions into machine language instructions.

■ assembly language

a machine oriented language in which mnemonics are used to represent each machine language instruction. Each CPU has its own specific assembly language.

■ assymetrical transmission

transmission which sends data at different rates in each direction, faster downstream than upstream.

■ asymmetry potential

the potential developed across the glass membrane with identical solutions on both sides. Also a term used when comparing glass electrode potential in pH 7 buffer.

■ asynchronous

a communication method where data is sent when it is ready without being referenced to a timing clock, rather than waiting until the receiver signals that it is ready to receive.

asynchronous transfer mode (atm)

a very high speed network utilising SONET optical transmission methods through the public telecommunications system.

AT cut

the commercial designation for a specifically oriented resonator plate, having desirable and repeatable operating characteristics. The "AT cut" is the most popular thickness-shear crystal unit manufactured today.

AT strip

an AT-cut crystal in the shape of a rectangular strip. It has a higher ESR than a round AT-cut crystal but is smaller in size, thus allowing smaller crystal packages.

ATC

Automatic temperature compensation.

ATM

the key emerging technology that uses fixed-length packets or cells to switch voice, data and video traffic over the local- and wide-area network.

atom

the basic component of all matter; the smallest particle of an element that can exist either alone or in combination. Each atom consists of a nucleus (containing neutrons and protons) and electrons.

attenuation

the relative decrease in amplitude of a given parameter. Attenuation measurements are common for voltage, current, and power. It is usually expressed in decibels (dB). For a power ratio, one dB = $10Log_{10}(P_1/P_2)$. For a current ratio, one dB = $20Log_{10}(I_1/I_2)$. For a voltage ratio, one dB = $10Log_{10}(V_1/V_2)$.

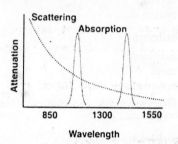

attenuation (insertion loss)

loss of power. Attenuation is usually measured in db loss per length of cable (ex. 31.0 db/100Ft.). Attenuation increases as frequency increases.

attenuator

a device used to attenuate a signal.

auto transformer

a transformer in which one winding or coil serves both the primary and secondary circuit.

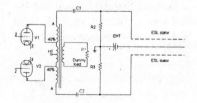

■ **automatic reset**

1. a feature on a limit controller that automatically resets the controller when the controlled temperature returns to within the limit bandwidth set. 2. the integral function on a PID controller which adjusts the proportional bandwidth with respect to the set point to compensate for droop in the circuit, i.e., adjusts the controlled temperature to a set point after the system stabilises.

■ **automatic substation**

indicates that the substation equipment will operate by itself in a pre-programmed manner, triggered by certain circumstances and conditions.

■ **auto-zero**

an automatic internal correction for offsets and/or drift at zero voltage input.

■ **average value**

the average of the instantaneous values through which an alternating voltage or current passes during one alternation. The average value of a sine curve is equal to .637 times its peak value.

■ **American wire gauge (AWG)**

a gauging system used to size wire. Every increase of 3 wire gauges is a 50% reduction in cross sectional area of the wire.

■ **axial thrust**

the force or loads that are applied to the motor shaft in a direction parallel to the axis of the shaft.

(Such as from a fan or pump)

■ **axis**

a direction in a quartz stone. The plural of "axis" is "axes."

■ **axis of rotation (spin axis)**

the axis of rotation (spin axis) is that straight line about which a body rotates.

■ **b channel**

in ISDN, a full duplex, 64 kbps channel sending data.

■ **back end of a motor**

the back end of a normal motor is the end which carries the coupling or driving pulley. (NEMA) This is sometimes called the drive end (D.E., pulley end P.E.) etc.

■ **back reflection (fiber optic)**

a measure of the light reflected off the polished end of a fiber connector. Measured in negative db relative to incident power.

■ **backbone**

the major multi-channel link in a network, from which smaller links branch.

■ **backbone network**

the main artery or link for a private or public network. Typically the backbone carries the lion's share of traffic (data, voice, video or some combination), is capable of carrying significant bandwidth and it is the network to which small/remote networks/links are attached.

■ **backbone wiring**

the cabling used between telecommunication closets, entrance facilities, equipment rooms, or buildings.

■ back-cover

enclosure on back of control which houses the electrical and mechanical components.

■ background noise

the total noise floor from all sources of interference in a measurement system, independent of the presence of a data signal.

■ backshell

a mechanical backing that is sometimes put onto a connector. The device protects the conductors and can be assembled or injection molded. Commonly used with D-Sub connectors.

■ backup

a system, device, file or facility that can be used as an alternative in case of a malfunction or loss of data.

■ balanced input

a differential input circuit pair with equal impedance to ground on each side. See **differential input**. The advantages as opposed to single-ended transmission are noise rejection over long distances of cabling.

■ balanced output

a differential output circuit pair with equal source impedance on each side. See **differential output**.

■ ballast

an electrical device used in fluorescent and HID fixtures. It furnishes the necessary starting and operating characteristics to the lamp for proper performance.

■ BALUN

an acronym for BALanced/ UNbalanced. A device commonly used to change one cabling media to another (ex. coaxial to twisted pair balun).

■ balun filter

input line filter often used on DC-DC converters that include a differential wound transformer. Balun filters present a low impedance to differential mode signals and a high impedance of common mode signals.

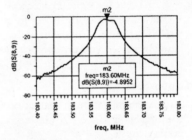

■ band pass

the frequency range over which an inductor or capacitor exhibits a low impedance.

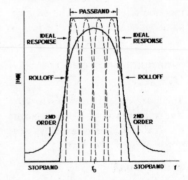

■ band stop

the frequency range over which

an inductor or capacitor exhibits a high impedance.

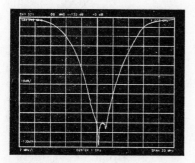

■ **bandwidth**

the measure of a circuit's ability to pass a full amplitude signal over a range of signal frequencies. Normally measured between the point or points where the signal amplitude falls to -3dB below the passband frequency. Normally defines the "frequency range" of a device or system.

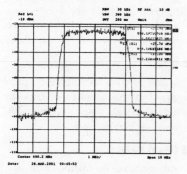

■ **bank**

actually, "transformer bank" or "capacitor bank;" a group of transformers or capacitors connected together.

■ **base**

the lower portion of a crystal holder. The base incorporat

resonator mounting structure and leads or pins to connect the device to an external circuit. See also **ı holder**."

■ **base plate**

substrate to which circuit components are mounted or, a metal plate to which the converter is attached. Normally used to draw heat away from critical circuit components. Also see **heat sink**.

■ **base plate temperature**

see **case temperature**.

■ **base resistance**

the resistance of a polyswitch device under specified conditions (e.g.,20 °C), before connection into a circuit. Devices of a particular type will be delivered with a range of resistances; therefore, a minimum value, R_{min}, and/or a maximum value, R_{max}, are often given.

■ **base speed, rpm**

the speed which a DC motor develops at rated armature and field voltage with rated load applied.

■ **baseband**

transmission scheme in which the entire bandwidth, or data-carrying capacity, of a medium (such as coaxial cable) is used to carry a single digital pulse, or a signal, between multiple users. Because digital signals are not modulated, only one kind of data can be transmitted at a time. Contrast with broadband.

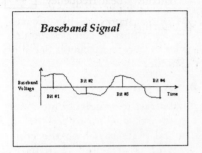

baseband transmission

a transmission method where direct current signals are placed directly onto the transmission medium (cable). Ethernet is a baseband network type, hence, the "Base" in 10Base-T, etc.

BASIC

a high-level programming language designed at Dartmouth College as a learning tool. Acronym for Beginner's All-purpose Symbolic Instruction Code.

batch process

any process on which operations are carried out on a limited number of articles, as opposed to continuous process.

bathymetry

measurement of the depths of features at the bottom of the sea, especially by echo-sounding.

battery

any energy-storage device allowing release of electricity on demand. It is made up of one or more electrical cells. Primary-cell batteries are disposable; secondary-cell batteries, or accumulators, are rechargeable. Primary-cell batteries are an extremely uneconomical form of energy, since they produce only 2% of the power used in their manufacture. The lead-acid car battery is a secondary-cell battery. The car's generator continually recharges the battery. It consists of sets of lead (positive) and lead peroxide (negative) plates in an electrolyte of sulphuric acid (battery acid). The introduction of rechargeable nickel-cadmium batteries has revolutionized portable electronic newsgathering (sound recording, video) and information processing (computing). These batteries offer a stable, short-term source of power free of noise and other electrical hazards.

battery backup

subsystem for electronic equipment that provides power in the event of input power loss. Battery backed systems are a common application are for DC-DC converters.

baud

a unit of data transmission speed equal to the number of bits (or signal events) per second; 300 baud = 300 bits per second.

baud rate

the signaling or symbol rate of a digital transmission path or device. A symbol can represent more than one bit of information, depending on the encoding or modulation scheme used to create the symbol. Often used interchangeably with bits per second (BPS), although incorrectly.

■ bauxite

the raw material mined from the earth we use to make aluminum.

■ bcd, buffered

binary-coded decimal output with output drivers, to increase line-drive capability.

■ bcd, parallel

a digital data output format where every decimal digit is represented by binary signals on four lines and all digits are presented in parallel. The total number of lines is 4 times the number of decimal digits.

■ bcd, serial

a digital data output format where every decimal digit is represented by binary signals on four lines and up to five decimal digits are presented sequentially. The total number of lines is four data lines plus one strobe line per digit.

■ bcd, three-state

an implementation of parallel BCD, which has 0, 1 and high-impedance output states. The high-impedance state is used when the BCD output is not addressed in parallel connect applications.

■ bearing

a part which supports a journal and in which a journal revolves.

■ bearing life

rating life, L_{10} (B_{10}), is the life in hours or revolutions in which 90% of the bearings selected will obtain or exceed. Median life (average life), L_{50}(B_{50})

■ bearing RTD

a probe used to measure bearing temperature to detect an overheating condition. The RTD's resistance varies with the temperature of the bearings.

■ bearings

are used to reduce friction and wear while supporting rotating elements. For a motor it must provide a relatively rigid support for the output shaft.

The bearing acts as the connection point between the rotating and stationary elements of a motor. There are various types such as roller, ball, sleeve (journal), and needle. The ball bearing is used in virtually all types and sizes of electric motors. It exhibits low friction loss, is suited for high speed operation and is compatible in a wide range of temperatures. There are various types of ball bearings such as open, single shielded or sealed. Reliance Electric offers a unique PLS bearing system.

■ beat frequency

beat frequencies are periodic vibrations that result from the addition and subtraction of two or more sinusoids. For example, in the case of two turbine aircraft engines that are rotating at nearly the same frequency but not precisely at the same frequency; Four frequencies are generated:(f1) the rotational frequency of turbine one, (f2) the rotational frequency of turbine two, (f1 + f2) the sum of turbine rotational frequencies one and two, and (f1 - f2) which is the difference or "beat" frequency of turbines one and two. The difference of the two frequencies is the lower frequency and is the one that is "felt" as a beat or "wow" in this case.

beryllia

BeO (Beryllium Oxide) a high-temperature mineral insulation material, toxic in powder form.

best fit straight line

a line midway between two parallel straight lines enclosing all output vs. pressure values.

beta ratio

the ratio of the diameter of a pipeline constriction to the unconstricted pipe diameter.

bevel

a modification to one or both of the major faces of a resonator plate in which the face is altered to have a partially spherical configuration. Also see "Contour."

B-H curve

curve to show characteristics of a magnetic material, in terms of magnetising force (H) and resulting flux density.

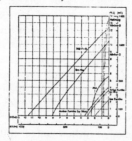

bhmax (maximum energy product)

indicates the maximum energy that a magnetic material can supply to an external magnetic circuit when operating at the Bd, Hd point on its demagnetisation curve, measured in mega Gauss-Oersteds (MGOe) or kiloJoules per cubic meter (kJ/m3).

bias current

a very low-level DC current generated by the panel meter and superimposed on the signal. This current may introduce a measurable offset across a very high source impedance.

bibo stable

a system is bounded-input bounded-output stable if bounded inputs get mapped to bounded outputs. An LTI system is BIBO stable if and only if its impulse response is absolutely integrable.

bifilar winding

two strands of magnet wire wound side-by-side.

big picture

generally, feedback control system design seeks to design a controller K for a plant P based on a nominal model Po for P such that the resulting nominal closed loop system (with Po and K) exhibits the following properties: stability, stability robustness with respect to realistic modelling errors, good low frequency command following (tracking), good low frequency disturbance rejection, and good high frequency noise attenuation, performance robustness with respect to realistic modelling errors.

bilateral contract

an agreement between two parties for the purchase and sale of energy products and services.

binary

refers to base 2 numbering system, in which the only allowable digits are 0 and 1. Pertaining to a condition that has only two possible values or states.

binary coded decimal

the representation of a decimal number (base 10, 0 through 9) by means of a 4 bit binary nibble.

BCD		Decimal
0000	=	0
0001	=	1
0010	=	2
0011	=	3
0100	=	4
0101	=	5
0110	=	6
0111	=	7
1000	=	8
1001	=	9

binned

binned refers to resistance-matched devices, which are supplied such that all parts in one particular package (or reel) are within 0.5 ohms of each other (1.0 ohms for TR250-080T devices). Individual matched packages are supplied from the full resistance range of the specified device. The benefit is that resistance-matched devices reduce the tip-ring resistance differential, reducing the possibility of line imbalance. Sorted devices are those that are supplied with resistance values that are within specified segments of the device's full range of resistance, giving greater design flexibility. Synonyms: Sorted

biodegradable

capable of being broken down by living organisms, principally bacteria and fungi.

biomass

biomass energy is derived from plants. Alcohol fuels are produced from wood, sugarcane and corn. Firewood, crop residue and cattle dung can also be burned as biomass fuel. As long as the amount of plants regrown equals the amount of fuel burned there will be no additional carbon dioxide produced to contribute toward global warming.

BIOS

acronym for basic input/output system. The commands used to tell a CPU how it will communicate with the rest of the computer.

bipolar

the ability of a panel meter to display both positive and negative readings.

bipolar transistor

a transistor which operates by the action of minority carriers across a P/N junction; and is a current controlled device as opposed to a voltage controlled device.

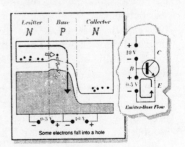

■ bit

acronym for binary digit. The smallest unit of computer information, it is either a binary 0 or 1.

■ bit error rate

the ratio of received bits that are in error.

■ bits per second

the number of bits passing a point every second. The transmission rate for digital information.

■ blackbody

a theoretical object that radiates the maximum amount of energy at a given temperature, and absorbs all the energy incident upon it. A blackbody is not necessarily black. (The name blackbody was chosen because the colour black is defined as the total absorption of light energy.)

■ blank

a quartz resonator plate. Also known as a "wafer," a "plate," or a "resonator."

■ blanking/blanking interval

the period of time when a television monitor is "blanked" while the electron beam retraces from right to left or bottom to top. In a baseband video signal, the intervals between active video lines and between the last active line in a field and the first active line in the next. Ideally, a video switcher would sense when a blanking period occurs and would switch the video signal during this time. This prevents any visually unpleasant video effects on a monitor. This requires the video switcher to actively monitor each of the user's video sources.

■ blec

building local exchange carrier

■ bleeder resistor

a resistor added to a circuit for the purpose of providing a small current drain, usually to provide a load for improving output voltage stability, or to assure discharge of capacitors.

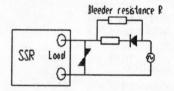

■ block diagram

a diagram which shows how the subsystems of a system are interconnected.

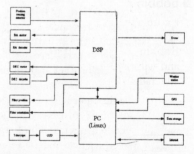

■ blocking

a term with multiple and conflicting industry usage. 1) May be used to express the inability to connect a single input of a switching array to multiple outputs simultaneously without any input loading or mismatches. If multiple outputs are connected to a given input, proportional input loading will occur. 2) In multi-stage switching arrays (tri-stage or 3-stage), it refers to the possibility that the user may not be able to route an input to an output at all times (blocking due to unavailable middle stages). It is possible that even if blocking occurs, the switching array may be able to be reinitialised in a logical order to avoid the blocking conditions.

■ bnc

A quick disconnect electrical connector used to inter-connect and/ or terminate coaxial cables.

■ bobbin

a device upon which the windings of a transformer or inductor are wound, which provides a form for the coil and insulates the windings from the core.

■ bobbin core

a core with the shape of a bobbin or spool which contains flanges. Bobbin cores are available with and without leads and in the axial and radial form.

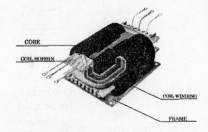

■ bode plot

defined for an LTI system with transfer function H; refers to two plots: (i) a plot of $20\log_{10}|H(jw)|$

versus $\log_{10}(w)$ on a semilog graph called the magnitude response or spectrum and (ii) a plot of angle of $H(jw)$ versus $\log\_10\ w$ on a semilog graph called the phase response or spectrum. Also referred to as the frequency response or spectrum of the system H.

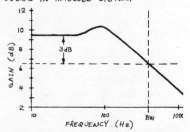

BANDWIDTH (BW) OF LOW PASS CIRCUIT USING AN AUTOBODE SYSTEM

■ boiling point

the temperature at which a substance in the liquid phase transforms to the gaseous phase; commonly refers to the boiling point of water which is 100°C (212°F) at sea level.

■ bonding jumper

a bare or insulated conductor used to ensure the required electrical conductivity between metal parts required to be electrically connected. Frequently used from a bonding bushing to the service equipment enclosure to provide a path around concentric knockouts in an enclosure wall: also used to bond one raceway to another.

■ boost regulator

a basic DC-DC switching converter topology that takes an unregulated input voltage and produces a higher regulated output voltage. The higher output voltage is achieved by storing energy in an input inductor and then transferring the energy to the output by turning a shunt switch (transistor) on and off at a fast rate.

bps

the amount of binary data sent in bits per second. Not to be confused with baud rate. Modern data and fax modems, for example, transmit at 14,400 bits per second using a baud rate of 2,400 baud. This is accomplished by complex encoding methods. Also used as a general term to define any rate that digital data flows .

brakes

an external device or accessory that brings a running motor to a standstill and/or holds a load. Can be added to a motor or incorporated.

braking torque

the torque required to bring a motor down to a standstill. The term is also used to describe the torque developed by a motor during dynamic braking conditions.

branch circuit

that part of a wiring circuit between the final set of fuses and the place where the lighting fixtures or drop cords are attached.

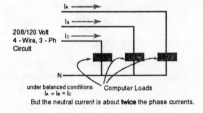

208/120 Volt
4 - Wire, 3 - Ph
Circuit

under balanced conditions   Computer Loads
Iₐ = Iₐ = Ic
But the neutral current is about **twice** the phase currents.

break parallel

to open the switch that ties or connects two circuits together.

breakaway

a routing control mode wherein an audio source can be selected independently of the video source and vice versa.

break-before-make

disconnecting the present circuit before connecting a new circuit. Also known as Break/Make.

breakdown torque

the maximum torque a motor will develop at rated voltage without a relatively abrupt drop or loss in speed.

breakdown voltage

a voltage level at which dielectric insulation fails by excessive leakage current or arcing. In reference to power supplies the breakdown voltage is the maximum AC or DC voltage that can be applied from input to output and/or chassis.

breakdown voltage rating

the dc or ac voltage which can be applied across insulation portions of a transducer without arcing or conduction above a specific current value.

breaker

a safety device to sense overloading and interrupt the circuit.

breakover current

instantaneous current flowing at the breakover voltage, VBO.

■ breakover voltage

maximum voltage across a SiBar device at breakdown measured under a specified voltage rate of rise and current rate of rise. Synonyms: System Damage Voltage

■ bridge

a networking component that links two or more network segments. Bridges are used to split busy networks into separate, less congested segments.

■ bridge converter

switching converter topology that employs four switching elements (full bridge) or two switching elements (half-bridge). This topology is more often used in off-line supplies rather than DC-DC converters. Bridge converters provide high output power and low ripple, but are significantly more complex than other types of converter topologies and thus are more expensive and prone to failure. Also see Boost Regulator, Buck Regulator, Flyback Converter, Foward Converter, Push-Pull Converter and Resonant Converter.

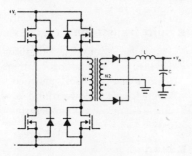

■ bridge rectifier

a full wave rectifier circuit employing four rectifiers in a bridge configuration.

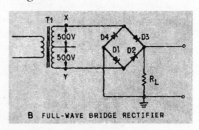

B FULL-WAVE BRIDGE RECTIFIER

■ bridge resistance

see **input impedance** and **output impedance**.

■ bridge/router

a device that can provide the function of a bridge, router or both concurrently. Bridge/router can route one or more protocols, such as TCP/IP and/or XNS, and bridge all other traffic.

■ broadband

data transmission at a high rate, generally greater than T1 speeds (1.5 Mbps). This allows the transmission of voice, data and video signals over a single medium.

■ broadband transmission

a transmission method where multiple channels are modulated onto separate carrier frequencies. The result is multiple communications channels that occupy specific frequency ranges.

■ brownout

a reduction of the AC mains' distribution voltage, usually caused deliberately by the utility company to reduce power consumption when demand exceeds generation or distribution capacity.

brownout protection

the ability of a power supply to continue operating within specification through the duration of a brownout.

brush

a piece of current conducting material (usually carbon or graphite) which rides directly on the commutator of a commutated motor and conducts current from the power supply to the armature windings.

bsp

broadband service provider

BT cut

the commercial designation for a specifically oriented resonator plate, having well known and repeatable characteristics. The "BT cut" is less popular than the "AT."

btu

a British Thermal Unit. A measure of energy in the English system measurement, roughly the amount of heat required to raise one pound of water one degree Fahrenheit. This unit of measuring heat will soon no longer be used and will be replaced in usage by "joule."

buck boost converter

see flyback converter

buck derived converter

see **forward converter**

buck regulator

a basic DC-DC switching converter topology that takes an unregulated input voltage and pro-

duces a lower regulated output voltage. The lower output voltage is achieved by chopping the input voltage with a series connected switch (transistor) which applies pulses to an averaging inductor and capacitor.

buckarm

a crossarm placed on a pole parallel to the main line conductors.

buffer

1. a storage area for data that is used to compensate for a speed difference, when transferring data from one device to another. Usually refers to an area reserved for I/O operations, into which data is read, or from which data is written.

2. any substance or combination of substances which, when dissolved in water, produces a solution which resists a change in its hydrogen ion concentration on the addition of an acid or alkali.

bulb (liquid-in-glass thermometer)

the area at the tip of a liquid-in-glass thermometer containing the liquid reservoir.

burd transformer

stands for "Buried Underground Residential Distribution." A transformer that is normally located in an enclosure, below ground level, and is energized with underground cable.

burn in

operation of newly manufactured converters for some period of time prior to shipment.

The intent is to stabilise the converter and eliminate infant mortality by aging the device. The time period and conditions (input power cycling, load switching, temperature, etc.) varies from vendor to vendor. However, the less stringent the conditions, the less likely it is that potential problems will be caught by the vendor.

■ **burst pressure**

the maximum pressure applied to a transducer sensing element or case without causing leakage.

■ **burst proportioning**

a fast-cycling output form on a time proportioning controller (typically adjustable from 2 to 4 seconds) used in conjunction with a solid state relay to prolong the life of heaters by minimising thermal stress.

■ **bus**

parallel lines used to transfer signals between devices or components. Computers are often described by their bus structure (i.e., S-100, IBM PC).

■ **bushing**

an insulator attached to a piece of electrical equipment, such as a capacitor or transformer. The capacitor keeps an energized conductor insulated from the equipment.

■ **bus-powered**

class of devices that derive their power from the main Hub. Examples include USB hubs, keyboards, mice, internet cameras.

■ **butt gap**

a gap, mostly found in E cores, that is obtained by equally spacing all mating surfaces of the core, usually by plastic shims or some other non-magnetic material. This is an alternative to centre post gapping, where only the centre leg of a core is gapped. To achieve the same gap electrically a centre leg gap must be twice as much as a butt gap.

■ **bypass**

device used to maintain service while testing or replacing a meter.

■ **byte**

the representation of a character in binary. Eight bits.

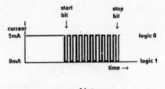

1 byte

■ **C flange**

a type of flange used with close coupled pumps, speed reducers, and similar applications where the mounting holes in the f flange are threaded to receive bolts. Normally the "C" Flange is used where a pump or similar item is to be overhung on the motor. The "C" type flange is a NEMA standard design and available with or without feet.

■ **C.I**

the abbreviation for "crystal impedance," sometimes used in place of the word "resistance."

■ C.I.F.

cut in Flat.

■ C.I.M

the abbreviation for "crystal impedance meter." See "**test set**"

■ C0

the abbreviation for "**shunt capacitance.**"

■ C1

the abbreviation for "Motional Capacitance." Motional capacitance is also often abbreviated as "Cm."

■ cable

a set of insulated wires or conductors within an extruded jacket. Many types of cable utilise shielding around the wires and under the cable jacket.

■ cable assembly

a piece of cable that has been terminated with one or more connectors.

■ cable modem

modem designed for use on TV coaxial cable circuit.

■ calender-van dusen equation

an equation that defines the resis-

tance-temperature value of any pure metal that takes the form of $R_T = R_O(1 + AT + BT^2)$ for values between the ice point (0°C) and the freezing point of antimony (630.7°C) and the form $R_T = R_O[1 + AT + BT^2 + C(T-100)T^2]$ between the oxygen point (-183.0°C) and the ice point (0°C).

■ calibration

the process of adjusting an instrument or compiling a deviation chart so that its reading can be correlated to the actual value being measured.

■ calorie

currently the most common unit for measuring heat and soon to be replaced by joules (J). The calorie is the amount of energy required to raise the temperature of one cubic centimeter of water one degree Celsius (formerly called centigrade). The calorie is from the Latin word "calor" meaning "heat." It is equivalent to 4.185 joules). It is important not to confuse the word calorie (small c) with Calorie (capital C). A Calorie (or kilocalorie) describes the available energy in food. It is the amount of heat required to raise the temperature of 1,000 grams (Kilogram) of water by 1 degree Celsius. Physicist Paul Hewitt put it this way: "To the weight watcher, the peanut contains 10 Calories. To the physicist, it releases 10,000 calories (or 41,850 joules) of energy when burned or digested.

■ campus area network

a network which encompasses interconnectivity between floors of a building and/or buildings in a confined geographic area such as a campus or industrial park. Such networks would not require public rights-of-way and operate over fairly short distances.

■ candle power

a measure of light.

■ canopy (dripcover)

a protective cover placed on the top of a motor being mounted vertically to protect it from liquids or solids that might drop onto the motor. (It acts similar to an umbrella for the motor.)

■ CAP

Carrierless Amplitude Phase Modulation. A two-dimensional line code used in ADSL.

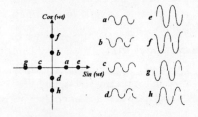

■ capacitance

the property exhibited by two conductors separated by a dielectric whereby an electric charge becomes stored between the conductors. Capacitance is measured in "farads" and is identified by the letter "C."

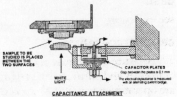

SAMPLE TO BE
STUDIED IS PLACED
BETWEEN THE
TWO SURFACES

WHITE
LIGHT

CAPACITOR PLATES
Gap between the plates is 0.1 mm

The electrical capacitance is measured
with an alternating current bridge.

CAPACITANCE ATTACHMENT
SURFACE FORCES APPARATUS

■ capacitive coupling

coupling of a signal between two circuits, due to discrete or parasitic capacitance between the circuits.

■ capacitor

a device which, when connected in an alternating-current circuit, causes the current to lead the voltage in time phase. The peak of the current wave is reached ahead of the peak of the voltage wave. This is the result of the successive storage and discharge of electric energy used in 1 phase motors to start or in 3 phase for power factor correction.

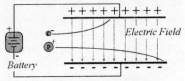

PARALLEL PLATE CAPACITOR

Electric Field

Battery

CREATING AN
ELECTRIC FORCE FIELD

■ capacitor bank

a group of capacitors connected together for three-phase application

■ capacitor motor

a single-phase induction motor with a main winding arranged for direct connection to the power source, and auxiliary winding connected in series with a capacitor. There are three types of capacitor motors: capacitor start, in which the capacitor phase is in the circuit only during starting, permanent-split capacitor, which has the same capacitor and capacitor phase in the circuit for both starting and running; two-value capacitor motor, in which there are different values of capacitance for starting and running.

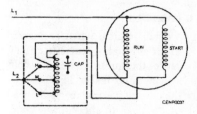

capacitor start

the capacitor start is a single phase motor is basically the same as the split phase start, except that it has a capacitor in series with the starting winding. The addition of the capacitor provides a more ideal phase relation and results in greater starting torque with much less power input. As in the case of the split phase motor, this type can be reversed at rest, but not while running unless special starting and reversing switches are used. When properly equipped for reversing while running, the motor is much more suitable for this service than the split phase start as it provides greater reversing ability at less watts input.

capacity

the ability to hold or carry an electric charge.

CAPS

competative Access Provider or Competative Local Exchange Carrier. Alternative provider to Local Exchange Carrier.

carbon dioxide (CO2)

a colourless, odorless, nonflammable gas formed during decomposition, combustion and respiration. CO_2 is used in food refrigeration (dry ice), carbonated beverages (the bubbles and fizz), fire extinguishers and aerosol cans. Whenever something burns — such as gasoline, wood or a candle — CO_2 is produced from the available oxygen combined with the carbon in the fuel.

carbon monoxide (CO)

colourless, odorless gas formed when carbon is oxidised in a limited supply of air. It is a poisonous constituent of car exhaust fumes, forming a stable compound with hemoglobin in the blood, thus preventing the hemoglobin from transporting oxygen to the body tissues.

carbonyl iron

a relatively expensive iron powder used in low permeability, high frequency powdered iron cores.

carrier frequency method

scanning method used mainly with magnetic and inductive measuring systems.

carry current

see cold switching.

case

see enclosure.

case temperature

temperature of the case when the converter and surrounding system are operating normally. Often used as a specification for DC-DC converters with extended temperature ranges. Case temperature is at times referred to as a Base Plate Temperature.

■ **category 5**

the minimum standard unshielded twisted pair cabling used for LAN drops.

■ **cathode**

in a diode, the electrode that must be negative with respect to the anode (plate) to allow the diode to conduct.

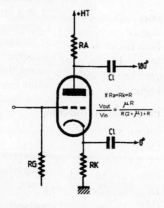

■ **cation**

a positively charged ion (Na⁺, H⁺).

■ **cavitation**

the boiling of a liquid caused by a decrease in pressure rather than an increase in temperature.

■ **CDMA**

code division multiple access

■ **celsius (centrigrade)**

a temperature scale defined by 0°C at the ice point and 100°C at boiling point of water at sea level.

■ **centre conductor**

the solid or stranded wire in the middle of the coaxial cable. The conductor diameter is measured by the American Wire gauge (AWG).

■ **centre frequency**

the midpoint in the passband.

■ **centre of gravity (mass centre)**

the centre of gravity of a body is that point in the body through which passes the resultant of weights of its component particles for all orientations of the body with respect to a uniform gravitational field.

■ **centre tap**

an electrical connection made at the centre of a transformer or inductor winding, usually so as to result in an equal number of turns on either side of the tap.

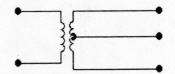

■ **centering**

the act of setting the output voltage of a power supply under specified load conditions, usually an auxiliary output of a multiple output power supply with all outputs at half load.

■ **centrifugal cutout switch**

a centrifugally operated automatic mechanism used in conjunction with split phase and other types of single phase induction motors. Centrifugal cutout switches will open or disconnect the starting winding when the rotor has reached a pre-determined speed, and reconnect it when the motor speed falls below it. Without such a device, the starting winding would be susceptible to rapid overheating and subsequent burnout.

■ centripetal force

a force exerted on an object moving in a circular path which is exerted inward toward the centre of rotation.

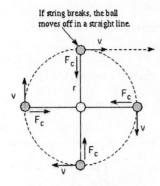

If string breaks, the ball moves off in a straight line.

$$F_c = m v^2 / r$$

Just enough centripetal force F_c to balance the speed; just enough speed to balance the centripetal force.

■ ceramic

polycrystalline ferroelectric materials which are used as the sensing units in piezoelectric accelerometers. There are many different grades, all of which can be made in various configurations to satisfy different design requirements.

■ ceramic cores

one of the common materials used for inductor cores. Its main purpose is to provide a form for the coil. In some designs it also provides the structure to hold the terminals in place. Ceramic has a very low thermal coefficient of expansion, which allows for relatively high inductance stability over the operating temperature ranges. Ceramic has no magnetic properties. Thus, there is no increase in permeability due to the core material. Ceramic core inductors are often referred to as air core inductors. Ceramic core inductors are most often used in high frequency applications where low inductance values, very low core losses, and high Q values are required.

■ ceramic insulation

high-temperature compositions of metal oxides used to insulate a pair of thermocouple wires The most common are Alumina (Al_2O_3), Beryllia (BeO), and Magnesia (MgO). Their application depends upon temperature and type of thermocouple. High-purity alumina is required for platinum alloy thermocouples. Ceramic insulators are available as single and multihole tubes or as beads.

■ CFM

cubic feet per minute, which is a measure of the volume of air flowing in a system.

■ channel

a communication path. Multiple channels can be multiplexed over a single cable in certain environments. The term is also used to describe the specific path between large computers and attached peripherals.

channel crosstalk

coupling of a signal from one channel to another or any other output by conduction or radiation. Crosstalk is expressed in decibels (dB) at a specified load impedance and over a specific frequency range or ranges.

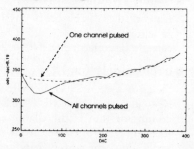

character

a letter, digit or other symbol that is used as the representation of data. A connected sequence of characters is called a character string.

charge

the number of electrons held on the capacitor plates. The act of forcing electrons onto the capacitor plates.

charge sensitivity

for accelerometers that are rated in terms of charge sensitivity, the output voltage (V) is proportional to the charge (Q) divided by the shunt capacitance (C). This type of accelerometer is characterised by a high output impedance. The sensitivity is given in terms of

charge; picocoulombs per unit of acceleration (g).

charged

the condition of a capacitor which has the full charge it can receive from a given applied voltage.

chatter

the rapid cycling on and off of a relay in a control process due to insufficient bandwidth in the controller.

check meter

an instrument used to establish the amount of electricity used by a customer's appliances.

chlorofluorocarbon (cfc)

synthetic chemical that is odorless, nontoxic, nonflammable, and chemically inert. CFCs have been used as propellants in aerosol cans, as refrigerants in refrigerators and air conditioners, and in the manufacture of foam packaging. They are partly responsible for the destruction of the ozone layer.

choke

an inductor which is intended to filter, or choke, out unwanted signals.

chroma

the colour portion of a video signal "C".

■ chromega®

a chromium-nickel alloy which makes up the positive leg of type K and type E thermocouples (registered trademark of OMEGA ENGINEERING, INC.).

■ chromel

an alloy of nickel with about 10% chromium, used with Alumel in K-type thermocouples.

■ churn

a term used to describe turnover in subscribers of various media such as magazines, newspapers, cable, and videotex services. Churn is an important measures of a medium's success in holding on to customers after they have been signed up as subscribers.

■ circuit

the path taken by electrical current flowing through a conductor from one terminal of the source of supply to the other.

■ circuit breaker

an automatic switch which operates like a fuse and interrupts a circuit under an infrequent abnormal condition.

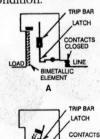

TRIP BAR
LATCH
CONTACTS
CLOSED
LOAD
LINE
BIMETALLIC
ELEMENT
A

TRIP BAR
LATCH
CONTACTS
OPEN
LOAD
LINE
BIMETALLIC
ELEMENT
BIMETAL HEATS AND BENDS
TO OPEN CONTACTS ON OvERLOAD
B

■ circuit switching

switching systems in which a dedicated physical circuit path must exist between sender and receiver for the duration of the "call". Used heavily in the phone company network, circuit switching often is contrasted with contention and token passing as a channel-access method, and with message switching and packet switching as a switching technique.

■ circuit-switched network

network that establishes a physical circuit temporarily, until it receives a disconnect signal.

■ circular mils (cm)

the cross sectional area of a circular conductor calculated as a square conductor (cm is the diameter squared). This is often used in power applications for current handling capability vs. temperature rise.

■ class 2 circuit

an isolated secondary circuit involving not more than 42.2 V (peak) with specific current level limitations.

■ clear

to restore a device to a prescribed initial state, usually the zero state.

■ clec

a distributed system model of computing that brings computing power to the desktop, where users("clients") access resources from servers.

■ client/server

a distributed system model of

computing that brings computing power to the desktop, where users("clients") access resources from servers.

■ **clipping**

the term applied to the phenomenon which occurs when an output signal is limited in some way by the full range of an amplifier, ADC or other device. When this occurs, the signal is flattened at the peak values, the signal approaches the shape of a square wave, and high frequency components are introduced. Clipping may be hard, as is the case when the signal is strictly limited at some level; or it may be soft, in which case the clipping signal continues to follow the input at some reduced gain.

■ **clips**

also known as JAWS. Point of contact between Edison meter and customer load. Customer responsibility.

■ **clock**

timing pulses used within a system or circuit to synchronise the operation of components. In a DC-DC converter, these pulses are used to synchronise operation of the PWM chips.

■ **close magnetic path**

magnetic core shapes designed to contain all of the magnetic flux generated from an excited winding(s). Inductors made with these core types are considered to be shielded inductors. Common core shapes that are considered to have closed magnetic paths are toroids, E-cores, and most pot cores. Shielded bobbins also offer a high degree of shielding but most of them have an air gap to some degree. Common core shapes that are considered to have open magnetic flux paths are rod cores and unshielded bobbin cores.

■ **closed circuits**

a complete electric circuit through which current will flow when voltage is applied.

■ **closed magnetic path**

magnetic core shapes designed to contain all of the magnetic flux generated from an excited winding(s). Inductors made with these core types are considered to be shielded inductors, although shielding is a matter of degree. Common core shapes that are considered to have closed magnetic paths are toroids, E-cores, and most pot cores. These core shapes do, however, contain minute air gaps that are unavoidable in manufacturing. Some common core shapes considered to have open magnetic flux paths are rod cores and unshielded bobbin cores.

■ **closed-on**

a complete circuit.

■ **closeness of control**

total temperature variation from a desired set point of system. Expressed as "closeness of control" is ±2°C or a system bandwidth with 4°C, also referred to as amplitude of deviation.

■ **clutch**

a mechanical device for engaging

and disengaging a motor often used when many starts and stops are required.

■ CMOS

the abbreviation for "Complementary Metal Oxide Semiconductor."

Copper CMP and Clean

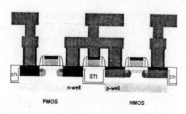

PMOS   NMOS

■ CMR (common-mode rejection)

the ability of a panel meter to eliminate the effect of AC or DC noise between signal and ground. Normally expressed in dB at dc to 60 Hz. One type of CMR is specified between SIG LO and PWR GND. In differential meters, a second type of CMR is specified between SIG LO and ANA GND (METER GND).

■ CMTS

cable modem termination system

■ CMV (common-mode voltage)

the AC or DC voltage which is tolerable between signal and ground. One type of CMV is specified between SIG LO and PWR GND. In differential meters, a second type of CMV is specified between SIG HI or LO and ANA GND (METER GND).

■ coal

coal is a form of stored solar energy. It is created from the remains of plants that have been concentrated by heat and pressure for millions of years. Coal is found in various forms or "grades," which depend on the ratio of carbon mass to energy content. Represented in descending order of hardness and energy content per pound, these grades are anthracite, bituminous, sub-bituminous and lignite.

■ coaxial adaptor

a device used to change one connector type to another or one gender to another (ex. BNC to SMA Adaptor).

■ coaxial cable

a cable that has one conductor (shield) completely surrounding the other (centre conductor), the two being coaxial and separated by an insulator. Standard industry types have a braided shield, or a semi-rigid copper or stainless steel shield material. Braided shield coaxial cable offers more physical flexibility but less shielding.

■ coaxial connector

the interconnection device found at each end of a coaxial cable assembly. There are many common types of coaxial connectors such as: BNC, SMA, SMB, F, etc.

■ coder/decoder (codec)

equipment to convert between analog and digital information format. It provides digital information format and digital compression functions.

■ coefficient of coupling (k)

a numerical rating between 0 and 1 that specifies the degree of magnetic coupling between two circuits. Maximum coupling is 1 and no coupling is 0.

■ coercive force (hc)

the value of magnetising force required to reduce the flux density to zero.

■ COFDM

code orthogonal frequency-division multiplexing

■ cogeneration

the use of waste heat from an electrical generating plant for other purposes, such as heating. Also, the use of waste heat from a high-temperature industrial process to generate electricity.

■ cogging

a term used to describe non-uniform angular velocity. It refers to rotation occurring in jerks or increments rather than smooth motion. When an armature coil enters the magnetic field produced by the field coils, it tends to speed up and slow down when leaving it. This effect becomes apparent at low speeds. The fewer the number of coils, the more noticeable it can be.

■ coherence function

a frequency domain function computed to show the degree of a linear, noise-free relationship between a system's input and output. The value of the coherence func-

tion ranges between zero and one, where a value of zero indicates there is no causal relationship between the input and the output. A value of one indicates, the existence of linear noise-free frequency response between the input and the output.

■ coil (stator or armature)

the electrical conductors wound into the core slot, electrically insulated from the iron core. These coils are connected into circuits or windings which carry independent current. It is these coils that carry and produce the magnetic field when the current passes through them. There are two major types: "Mush" or "random" wound, round wire found in smaller and medium motors where coils are randomly laid in slot of stator core; and formed coils of square wire individually laid in, one on top of the other, to give an evenly stacked layered appearance.

■ coils

another name for inductors.

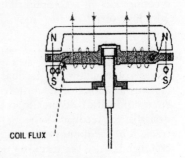

COIL FLUX

■ cold junction

the reference junction of a thermocouple which is kept at a constant temperature.

■ cold switching

closing the relay contacts before applying voltage and current, plus removing voltage and current before opening the contacts. (Contacts do not make or break current.) Also see **dry circuit switching**. Larger currents may be carried through the contacts without damage to the contact area since contacts will not "arc" when closed or opened.

■ cold weld

procedure in which the base and can are dissimilar metals that are pressed together to form one metal.

■ colour code

the ANSI established colour code for thermocouple wires in the negative lead is always red. Colour Code for base metal thermocouples is yellow for Type K, black for Type J, purple for Type E and blue for Type T.

■ com port

a connection on a computer into which a serial device may be plugged.

■ command following

refers to the ability of a feedback system to follow (or track) reference commands. Typically, it is desirable for feedback systems to track low frequency reference commands. Also see **tracking error**.

■ common

conductive path used as a return for two or more circuits. Common is often used interchangeably with ground, which is technically not correct unless it is connected to earth. Also see **ground**.

■ common carrier

licensed utility that provides communications services at government-regulated rates.

■ common mode

the output form or type of control action used by a temperature controller to control temperature, i.e. on/off, time proportioning, PID.

■ common mode current

a current conduction mode in which currents, present in two or more conductors, are flowing in phase and with equal magnitude within the conductor.

■ common mode filter (or choke)

an often used type of EMI filter which is wound in such a way that the phasing of the conductors will present a high impedance to common mode current (or noise) while presenting a low impedance to the desired signal.

■ common mode noise

noise present equally on two conductors with respect to some reference point; often used specifically to refer to noise present on both the hot and neutral AC lines with respect to ground.

■ common mode rejection

the ability of a differential input circuit to reject a signal common to both inputs, normally "hum" developed by 50 or 60 Hz power line (mains) voltages.

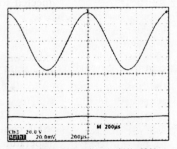

3. With a 5-V power supply and a 1-kHz, 60-V p-p common-mode signal (upper trace), the circuit's output (lower trace) illustrates the high common-mode rejection.

common mode rejection ratio

the ability of an instrument to reject interference from a common voltage at its input terminals with relation to ground. Usually expressed in db (decibels).

common mode type I

on a single phase Wye bus, the conduction mode in which phase, neutral, and ground currents are in phase. The return current path is through the ground plane and the case.

common mode type II

on a single phase Wye bus, the conduction mode in which phase and neutral currents are in phase, but the green wire currents are the return path, thus 180° out of phase.

common mode voltage

the voltage common to both sides of a differential circuit pair. The differential voltage across the cir-

cuit pair is the desired signal, whereas the common voltage signal is the unwanted signal which may have been coupled into the transmission pair.

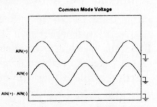

common-mode signal

a signal applied simultaneously to both inputs of a differential amplifier.

communication

transmission and reception of data among data processing equipment and related peripherals.

commutator

a cylindrical device mounted on the armature shaft and consisting of a number of wedge-shaped copper segments arranged around the shaft (insulated from it and each other. The motor brushes ride on the periphery of the commutator and electrically connect and switch the armature coils to the power source.

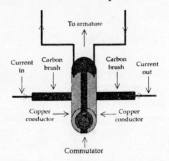

■ **compensated connector**

a connector made of thermocouple alloys used to connect thermocouple probes and wires.

■ **compensating alloys**

alloys used to connect thermocouples to instrumentation. These alloys are selected to have similar thermal electric properties as the thermocouple alloys (however, only over a very limited temperature range).

■ **compensating loop**

lead wire resistance compensation for RTD elements where an extra length of wire is run from the instrument to the RTD and back to the instrument, with no connection to the RTD.

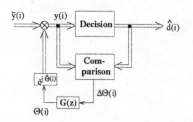

■ **compensation**

an addition of specific materials or devices to counteract a known error.

■ **compensator**

refers to a system which uses feedback measurements to generate control signals to a plant under control, the idea is to positively alter the properties of the plant in terms of measures such as command following, disturbance rejection, noise attenuation, sensitivity

to uncertainty, etc.. Also called controller.

■ **compiler**

A program that translates a high-level language, such as **basic**, into machine language.

■ **complementary root locus**

the complementary root locus for a negative feedback system with open loop transfer function L(s) = k n(s)/d(s) is a plot in the s-plane of the roots of the closed loop characteristic equation d(s) + k n(s) = 0 as the scalar constant k is varied from 0 to minus infinity. By so doing, one sees how the closed loop poles depend on the scalar constant and possibly a design parameter k. Also see **root locus.**

■ **complementary sensitivity transfer function**

given a negative feedback system with open loop transfer function L, the sensitivity transfer function denoted T is defined as follows: $T(s) = 1\ S(s) = L/(1 + L(s))$ where S denotes the sensitivity transfer function. See **sensitivity transfer** function.

■ **complete**

a complete test is a test which meets the requirements of IEEE-112-1978. It includes the tests conducted in a Routine Test as well as full-load heat run; no-load current and watts' determination of torques; efficiencies at 125, 100, 75, 50 and 25 percent of full load; power factor at 125, 100, 75, 50, and 25 percent of full load.

■ complex function

any mathematically defined relationship given by the following expression:

$$y(x) = a(x) + ib(x)$$

Where: x = the real variable

a(x) = the real part of $y(x)$

b(x) = the imaginary part of $y(x)$.

complex functions are usually expressed in terms of both their amplitude and phase.

■ complex wave

the resultant form of a number of sinusoidal waves that are summed together forming a periodic wave. Such waves may be analyzed in the frequency domain to readily determine their component parts.

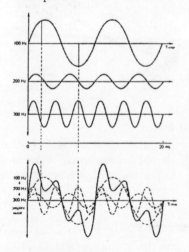

■ component video

a three-channel video signal wherein the luminance, hue and colour saturation information are carried as R, G and B (Red, Green and Blue) signals or as one of several variations of colour difference signals.

■ composite sync

a combination of horizontal and vertical sync pulses.

■ composite video

a single video signal carrying combined luminance, chrominance and raster synchronising information.

■ compound wound dc motors

designed with both a series and shunt field winding, the compound motor is used where the primary load requirement is heavy starting torque, and adjustable speed is not required. (See **paralleling**) Also used for parallel operation. The load must tolerate a speed variation from full-load to no-load. Industrial machine applications include large planers, boring mills, punch presses, elevators, and small hoists.

■ compression

reducing the size of a data set to lower the bandwidth or space required for transmission or storage.

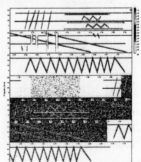

■ concentrator

device that serves as a wiring hub in star-topology network. Sometimes refers to a device containing multiple modules of network equipment.

■ condenser

two conductors separated by an insulating material that is capable of holding an electrical charge.

■ conditioned analog line

analog line to which devices have been added to improve the electrical signal.

■ conductance

the measure of the ability of a solution to carry an electrical current.

■ conduction

the conveying of electrical energy or heat through or by means of a conductor.

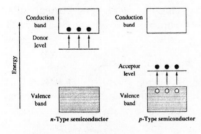

n-Type semiconductor   *p*-Type semiconductor

■ conduction cooled

cooling a converter via a solid material. Cools a power converter by adding a heat sink or attaching the module to the system chassis.

■ conductive polymer

a dispersion of conductive particles in an insulating organic polymer.

■ conductor

a material, such as copper or aluminum, which offers low resistance or opposition to the flow of electric current.

■ conduit

circular raceway that cable is run inside. Conduit requirements are specified under appropriate electrical code.

■ conduit box

the metal container usually on the side of the motor where the stator (winding) leads are attached to leads going to the power supply.

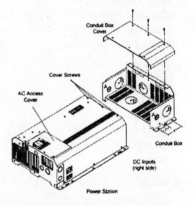

■ confidence level

the range (with a specified value of uncertainty, usually expressed in percent) within which the true value of a measured quantity exists.

■ conformity error

for thermocouples and RTDs, the difference between the actual reading and the temperature shown in published tables for a specific voltage input.

■ connection head

an enclosure attached to the end of a thermocouple which can be cast iron, aluminum or plastic within which the electrical connections are made.

■ connector

an electromechanical coupling device that provides an electrical interface that can be mated and unmated.

■ constant current power supply

a power supply designed to regulate the output current for changes in line, load, ambient temperature, and drift resulting from time.

■ constant h.p.

a designation for variable or adjustable speed motors used for loads requiring the same amount of H.P. regardless of their motor speed during normal operation.

■ constant speed

a DC motor which changes speed only slightly from a no load to a full load condition. In AC motors, these are synchronous motors.

■ constant torque

refers to loads whose H.P. requirements change linearly with changing speeds. Horsepower varies with the speed, i.e.- 2/1 HP at 1800/900 RPM. (Seen on some 2-speed motors). Possible applications include conveyors, some crushers, or constant-displacement pumps.

■ constant voltage power supply

a power supply designed to regulate the output voltage for changes in line, load, ambient temperature, and drift resulting from time.

■ constantan

an alloy of 40% nickel and 60% copper, with a high volume resistivity and almost negligible temperature coefficient. Used with copper in T-type thermocouples.

■ contact

the specific points of contact within a connector. Contacts can be male (pins) or female (sockets).

■ contact bounce

the intermittent and usually undesired opening of mechanical relay contacts during closure, or closing of contacts during opening. Contact bounce period depends upon the type of relay and varies from .5mS for small reed relays to 10-20mS for larger solenoid types. Solid-state or mercury wetted contacts (Hg) do not have a contact bounce characteristic.

■ contact emf

electromotive force which arises at the contact of dissimilar metals at the same temperature, or the same metal at different temperatures.

■ contact life

the maximum number of expected closures before failure. Life is dependent on the switched voltage, current, and power. Failure is usually when the contact resistance exceeds an end of life value. Typical failure mode is non-closure of the contact as opposed to a contact sticking closed.

contact potential

a voltage produced between contact terminals due to the temperature gradient across the relay contacts, and the reed-to-terminal junctions of dissimilar metals. (The temperature gradient is typically caused by the power dissipated by the energized coil.) Also known as contact offset voltage, thermal EMF, and thermal offset. This is a major consideration when measuring voltages in the microvolt range. There are special low thermal relay contacts available to address this need. Special contacts are not required if the relay is closed for a short period of time where the coil has no time to vary the temperature of the contact or connecting materials (welds or leads).

contact rating

the voltage, current, and power capacities of relay contacts under specified environmental conditions. See **carry current and switched current.**

contact resistance

resistance is basically the opposition to electron flow in an electrical circuit and connector manufacturers strive to attain the lowest amount of resistance possible for each contact. Contact resistance is the cumulative resistance value for mated contacts.

continuity

the state of being whole, unbroken.

continuous load

a load where the maximum current is expected to continue for three hours or more. Rating of the branch circuit protection device shall not be less tan 125% of the continuous load.

continuous process

method of producing an article continuously.

continuous shield

see **six-sided shielding**.

continuous spectrum

a frequency spectrum that is characterised by non-periodic data. The spectrum is continuous in the frequency domain and is characterised by an infinite number of frequency components.

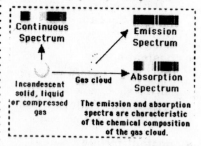

contour

a modification to one or both of the major faces of a resonator plate in which the face is altered to have a completely spherical configuration. Also see 'bevel.'

contract demand

a minimum demand charge based

on transformer capacity necessary to serve a customer's measurable demand.

■ **control character**

a character whose occurrence in a particular context starts, modifies or stops an operation that effects the recording, processing, transmission or interpretation of data.

■ **control circuit**

a circuit in a closed-loop system, typically containing an error amplifier, which controls the operation of the system to achieve regulation.

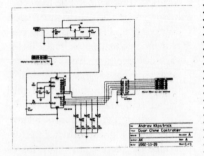

■ **control mode**

the output form or type of control action used by a temperature controller to control temperature, i.e., on/off, time proportioning, PID.

■ **control point**

the temperature at which a system is to be maintained.

■ **control voltage**

the range of voltage used to pull the frequency.

■ **control winding**

the winding on a mag amp or satu-

rable reactor used to control the amount of magnetic energy the core will absorb before saturating.

■ **controller (usb)**

device that provides the direct interface between the power switch device and the microprocessor. Enable and flag pin outputs connect directly into the power switch device.

■ **convection**

1. the circulatory motion that occurs in a fluid at a non-uniform temperature owing to the variation of its density and the action of gravity. 2. the transfer of heat by this automatic circulation of fluid.

■ **convection cooled**

cooling of a converter via the movement of air over the surface of its heat dissipating components. Free-air convection means that the natural movement of air (unassisted by a fan or blower) is sufficient to maintain a converter within specified operating limits.

■ **converter**

an electrical circuit which accepts a DC input and generates a DC output of a different voltage, usually achieved by high frequency switching action employing inductive and capacitive filter elements.

■ **cooling**

Removal of heat, which, in a power supply, is generated by transformation, rectification, regulation, and filtering. It can be accomplished using radiation, convection, forced air, or liquid means.

copper loss

the power lost by current flowing through the winding. The power loss is equal to the square of the current (I) multiplied by the resistance (R) of the wire (I2R). This power loss is realized in the form of heat.

copperoptics

a pairgain trademark referring to the functionality of the company's xDSL technology. In essence, with PairGain xDSL products, users can achieve fiber optic-quality signal transmission over copper cable.

core

the iron portion of the stator and rotor; made up of cylindrical laminated electric steel. The stator and rotor cores are concentric separated by an air gap, with the rotor core being the smaller of the two and inside to the stator core.

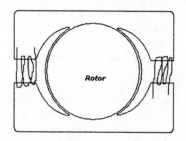

Rotor

core constant

the summation of the magnetic path lengths of each section of the magnetic circuit divided by the corresponding magnetic area of the same section.

core constant (C1) ([cm-1 ; mm-1])

the summation of the magnetic path length of each section of the circuit divided by the corresponding area of the same section.

core constant (C2) ([cm-3 ; mm-3])

the summation of the magnetic path length of each section of the magnetic circuit divided by the square of the corresponding magnetic area of the same section.

core losses

core losses are caused by an altering magnetic field in the core material. The losses are a function of the operating frequency and the total magnetic flux swing. The total core losses are made up of three main components: Hysteresis, eddy current and residual losses. These losses vary considerably from one magnetic material to another. Applications such as higher power and higher frequency switching regulators require careful core selection to yield the highest inductor performance by keeping the core losses to a minimum.

core saturation

see **saturation current**.

coriolis force

a result of centripetal force on a mass moving with a velocity radially outward in a rotating plane.

correction (balancing) plane

a plane perpendicular to the shaft axis of a rotor in which correction for unbalance is made.

coulomb

a measurement of the quantity of

electrical charge, usually expressed as pico coulomb (10^{-12} coulombs).

coulomb sensitivity

charge/unit acceleration, expressed in Pc/g (charge sensitivity).

counter electromotive force(cemf)

the induced voltage in a motor armature, caused by conductors moving through or "cutting" field magnetic flux. This induced voltage opposes the armature current and tends to reduce it.

counter weight

a weight added to a body so as to reduce a calculated unbalance at a desired place.

counts

the number of time intervals counted by the dual-slope A/D converter and displayed as the reading of the panel meter, before addition of the decimal point.

coupled mode

an unwanted mode that becomes energised at the same frequency as the desired mode, thereby draining energy from the desired mode.

coupler

a device used to connect two similar connector types.

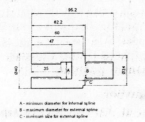

A - minimum diameter for internal spline
B - maximum diameter for external spline
C - minimum size for external spline

couplings

the mechanical connector joining the motor shaft to the equipment to be driven.

cover

the upper portion of a crystal holder, also referred to as a 'can.' Also see 'holder'

CPS

cycles per second; the rate or number of periodic events in one second, expressed in Hertz (Hz).

CPU

Central Processing Unit. The part of the computer that contains the circuits that control and perform the execution of computer instructions.

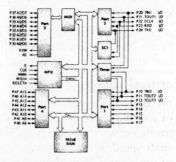

crest factor

In an AC circuit, Crest Factor is the mathematical ratio of the peak to RMS values of a waveform. Crest factor is sometimes used for describing the current stress in AC mains supply wires, since for a given amount of power transferred, the RMS value, and hence the losses, become greater with increasing peak values. Crest Factor gives essentially the same information as Power Factor, and is being replaced by Power Factor in power supply technology.

■ **crimping**

a means of securing an electrical contact to a wire using tools that compress the metal contact around the wire.

■ **critical damping**

critical damping is the smallest amount of damping at which a given system is able to respond to a step function without overshoot.

■ **critical rate of rise of off-state voltage**

maximum voltage rate of rise that will not cause a Si bar device to turn on.

■ **critical rate of rise of on-state current**

maximum current rate of rise a Si bar device can withstand without damage.

■ **critical speed**

the rotational speed of the rotor or rotating element at which resonance occurs in the system. The shaft speed at which at least one of the 'critical' or natural frequencies of a shaft is excited.

■ **critically damped poles**

refers to identical real poles which are stable (i.e. lie in the open left half plane). Such poles have a damping ratio zeta of unity and are associated with decaying exponentials in the time domain.

■ **cross connect**

The connection method used between permanent cabling (inside the walls) and equipment. A patch cord is often used as the connection means.

■ **cross regulation**

for a multiple output converter, the change in voltage on one output (expressed as a percent) caused by a load change on another output.

■ **crossarm**

an arm fastened at the top of a pole to separate and support conductors and apparatus.

■ **crosspoint switch**

a switch which, when closed, connects the signal on an input bus to one or more output buses. Also referred to as a matrix switch or switching array.

■ **crosstalk**

line static that can occur when wire pairs within the same bundles are used for separate signal transmission. Especially evident with repeated T1/E1 transmission.

■ **crosstalk/crosstalk isolation**

unwanted interference in an output resulting from other input and output signals, measured in dB below the nominal signal level, and is expressed in decibels (dB) at a specified load impedance and over a specific frequency range or ranges. Also referred to as All Hostile or Hostile Crosstalk. See **channel isolation**.

■ **crowbar**

circuit that crowbars or rapidly

shuts down a converters output if a preset voltage level is exceeded. The circuit places a low resistance shunt across the output when an overvoltage condition exists.

■ **crude oil**

crude oil is petroleum direct from the ground, prior to refinement or processing.

■ **cryogenics**

measurement of temperature at extremely low values, i.e., below -200°C.

■ **crystal**

a generic term used in place of the more complete expression 'piezoelectric quartz crystal unit.'

■ **CSU/DSU**

Channel Service Unit/Data Service Unit- A digital interface unit that connects end user equipment to the local digital telephone loop.

■ **cubic foot**

a unit of measurement for volume. It represents an area one foot long, by one foot wide, by one foot deep. Natural gas is measured in cubic feet, but the measurements are usually expressed in terms of Bcf, Tcf, Mcf, or Quads.

■ **cuk converter**

variation of the 'buck-boost' converter that produces very low output ripple. Used primarily in applications that do not require input/output isolation. Also see **flyback converter.**

■ **cure point**

the temperature at which a nor-

mally magnetic material goes through a magnetic transformation and becomes non-magnetic.

■ **curie temperature**

the temperature at which a ferrite material loses its magnetic properties. The cores permeability typically increases dramatically as the core temperature approaches the curie temperature, which causes the inductance to increase. The permeability drops to near unity at the curie temperature, which causes the inductance to drop dramatically. The curie point is the temperature at which the initial permeability (μi) has dropped to 10% of its value at room temperature.

Curie Temperature Vs. Fe Concentration

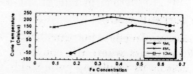

Approximate Curie temperature as a function of Fe concentration for three different thicknesses
♦ Maximum in Curie temperature occurs near x=0.4

■ **current**

current is often used to transmit signals in noisy environments because it is much less affected by environmental noise pick-up. Before A-D conversion the current signals are usually turned into voltage signals by a current-sensing resistor.

■ **current density**

the amperes per unit of cross section in the conductor. This is commonly measured in circular mils per amp (cm/A).

■ **current foldback**

see **foldback current limiting**.

■ **current limit**

maximum steady-state current level at which the power switch output is regulated in response to an overcurrent fault.

■ **current limit knee**

on a plot of output voltage vs current, the point at which current begins to limit (or foldback).

■ **current limiting**

feature that protects the converter (or load) from damage under overload conditions. The maximum converter output current is automatically limited to a predetermined safe value. If the converter is specified for auto restart, normal operation is automatically restored when overload condition is removed.

■ **current mode**

a control method for switch-mode converters where the converter adjusts its regulating pulse width in response to measured output current and output voltage, using a dual loop control circuit. Since output current is measured, current mode control allows accurate sharing between power supplies.

■ **current mode control**

control method used with switching converter topologies. A dual loop control circuit adjusts the PWM operation in response to a measured output current.

■ **current monitor**

an analog power supply signal which is linearly proportional to output current flow. Usually only feasible for single output power supplies.

■ **current proportioning**

an output form of a temperature controller which provides a current proportional to the amount of control required. Normally is a 4 to 20 milliamp current proportioning band.

■ **current rating**

is the maximum recommended DC current for the inductor. Expressed in milliamps (mA) or amps (A) maximum. This is limited by the allowable temperature rise.

■ **current surge limiting**

the circuitry necessary to protect relay contacts from excessive and possibly damaging current caused by capacitive loads.

■ **current transformer**

usually used in a sensing device, current transformers customarily have a one turn primary. The number of secondary turns is determined by the sensitivity required and is terminated with a resistor. Toroidal in shape, cores of silicon steel, nickel alloy, or ferrite are used. Choice of core material influences cost and accuracy.

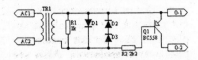

■ **current, maximum interrupt**

the highest fault current that can safely be used to trip a polyswitch device under specified conditions. Typically the lower the voltage dropped across the polyswitch device in its tripped state, the higher the maximum interrupt current. Maximum interrupt currents are usually shown in this Databook at the maximum voltage. It may be possible to use a polyswitch device at a higher interrupt current, but each such use must be individually qualified. Synonyms: Imax

■ **current, normal operating**

the highest steady state current that is expected to flow in a circuit under normal operating conditions. At the maximum ambient operating temperature of the circuit, the hold current of a polyswitch device used to protect the circuit is typically greater than the normal operating current.

■ **current, operating range**

the range of normal operating currents in a circuit containing a polyswitch device. Typically the hold current of the polyswitch device should be greater than the top of the operating current range.

■ **current, trip**

the smallest steady state current that, if passed through a polyswitch device, will cause the device to trip, under specified conditions. Synonyms: IT

■ **current, hold**

the largest steady state current that, under specified ambient conditions, can be passed through a polyswitch device without causing the device to trip. For SiBar devices, the cur-

rent at which the device resets to a high-impedance state once the surge current dissipates. See also **hold current**. Synonyms: IH,IHOLD

■ **curve fitting**

curve fitting is the process of computing the coefficients of a function to approximate the values of a given data set within that function. The approximation is called a 'fit'. A mathematical function, such as a least squares regression, is used to judge the accuracy of the fit.

■ **customer service conductors**

conductors between meter panel and Company service drops.

■ **cutout**

a term commonly used by operators to describe a distribution system fuse.

■ **CVR**

Conservation Voltage Regulation – Reduces transmission/distribution line voltages to conserve energy.

■ **cycle**

the complete set of values through which an alternating voltage or current passes successively.

■ **cycle time**

the time usually expressed in seconds for a controller to complete one on/off cycle.

■ **cycles per second (hertz)**

one complete reverse of flow of alternating current per rate of time. (A measure of frequency.) 60 HZ (cycles per second) A.C.

power is common throughout the U.S. and 50 HZ is more common in some foreign countries.

■ d channel

full duplex 16 kbps (basic rate) or 64 kbps (primary rate) ISDN channel.

■ d flange

a special end shield with holes for through bolts in the flange and is primarily used for mounting the motor on gear boxes or bulkheads. Standardised for frames 143T through 445T. 'D' flanges are not threaded and the bolt holes extend beyond the motor frame.

■ D.C. (Direct Current)

a current that flows only in one direction in an electric circuit. It may be continuous or discontinuous and it may be constant or varying.

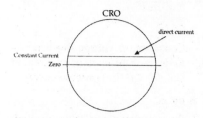

■ daisy chaining

the serial control connection of two or more mainframes in a master/slave(s) configuration. Also, some switching modules or cards can be daisy-chained to yield more inputs. This term is also used in reference to control panels daisy chaining (looping) from control panel to control panel to the final destination, the switching system.

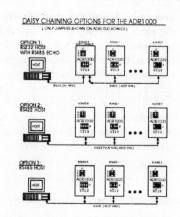

■ damping

the reduction of vibratory movement through dissipation of energy. Types include viscous, coulomb, and solid.

■ data acquisition

the automatic collection of data from sensors, instruments and devices: in a factory, laboratory or in the field.

■ data base

a large amount of data stored in a well-organised manner. A data base management system (DBMS) is a program that allows access to the information.

■ data circuit-terminating equipment

equipment that resides at the customer end of a transmission link and provides all necessary termination function for that link. May be owned by the customer or by the service provider.

■ data terminal equipment

the part of a data station that serves as a data source, destination, or both, and that provides for the data communications control function according to protocol. DTE includes computers, protocol translators, and multiplexers.

■ day-ahead market

the forward market for the supply of electrical power at least 24 hours before delivery.

■ dB (decibel)

20 times the log to the base 10 of the ratio of two voltages. Every 20 dBs correspond to a voltage ratio of 10, every 10 dBs to a voltage ratio of 3.162. For instance, a CMR of 120 dB provides voltage noise rejection of 1,000,000/1. An NMR of 70 dB provides voltage noise rejection of 3,162/1.

■ DC

Direct Current; an electric current flowing in one direction only and substantially constant in value.

■ dc bias

direct current (DC) applied to the winding of a core in addition to any time-varying current. Inductance with DC bias is a common specification for powder cores. The inductance will roll off gradually and predictably with increasing DC bias.

■ dc filter

a filter circuit that removes the AC ripple from a mostly DC current. Usually this is done by using an inductor and capacitor together.

■ dc gain

the dc gain of an LTI system with

transfer function H refers to the quantity H(0). The utility of this concept can be seen as follows. If the system H is stable and a step is applied then the steady state output of the system is H(o) times the size of the applied step.

■ dc motor

a motor using either generated or rectified D.C. power. A DC motor is usually used when variable speed operation is required.

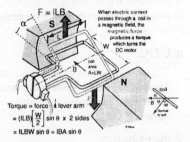

■ dc stress

annealing a magnetic material in the presence of a DC magnetic field to enhance magnetic properties.

■ dc-dc converter

a circuit or device that converts a DC input voltage (usually unregulated) to a regulated DC output voltage. The output voltage may be lower, higher, or the same as the input voltage. Switching regulator DC-DC circuits most often require an inductor or transformer to achieve the regulated output voltage. Switching regulator circuits can achieve a higher level of power efficiency when compared to non-switching techniques.

■ DCE

Data Communications Equipment

(EIA expansion) or Data Circuit-Terminating Equipment (CCITT expansion)- The devices and connections of a communications circuit with the end device (data terminal equipment). A modem can be considered a DCE.

■ **dcr (dc resistance)**

the resistance of an inductor to a DC current (not alternating). The DCR is most often minimised in the design of an inductor. The unit of measure is the Ohm, and is usually expressed as a maximum rating.

■ **DDC**

(Data Display Channel) is a standard that defines communication between a monitor and a host system.

■ **dead band**

1. for chart records: the minimum change of input signal required to cause a deflection in the pen position. 2. For temperature controllers: the temperature band where heat is turned off upon rising temperature and turned on upon falling temperature expressed in degrees. The area where no heating (or cooling) takes place.

■ **dead volume**

the volume of the pressure port of a transducer at room temperature and ambient barometric pressure.

■ **dead-leg**

de-energized phase, normally energized.

■ **debug**

to find and correct mistakes in a program.

■ **Debye-Huckel equation**

used in relating the activity coefficient (fi) to ion strength (see **Activity coefficient**): where I is the ionic strength, A and B the temperature-dependent constants (see Table A.5), Zi the valence of the ion (i), and Å the ion-size parameter in angstroms.

■ **decibels (db)**

the logarithmic ratio between two signal levels. In video and audio, it is normally defined as: $dB = 20 \log_{10}(V2/V1)$

■ **decimal**

refers to a base ten number system using the characters 0 through 9 to represent values.

■ **decoupling**

refers to a magnetic circuit where comparatively more of the flux generated by the MMF fringes around the magnetic material instead of entering it.

■ **dedicated line**

a transmission circuit installed between two sites of a private network and 'open,' or available, at all times.

■ **default**

the value(s) or option(s) that are assumed during operation when not specified.

■ **definite purpose motor**

a definite purpose motor is any motor design, listed and offered in standard ratings with standard operating characteristics with special mechanical features for use under service conditions other than usual or for use on a particular type of application.

■ degree

an incremental value in the temperature scale, i.e., there are 100 degrees between the ice point and the boiling point of water in the Celsius scale and 180°F between the same two points in the Fahrenheit scale.

■ delay margin

amount of time lag (time delay) which can be introduced into a feedback loop before the closed loop system goes unstable. Also see Gain Margin and Phase Margin.

■ delta system

a method of connecting three single transformers for three-phase application.

■ demagnetisation curve

that portion of the hysteresis loop that lies between the residual induction point (BR) and the coercive force point (HC).

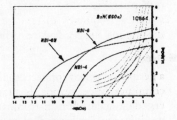

■ demagnetised

a material condition where a ringing AC field has reduced the remnant induction to or near zero. A ringing AC field is a continually de-

creasing sinusoidal field. A pulsed DC field can be used to achieve gross demagnetisation, but with much effort and with residual local magnetisation.

■ demand

the maximum amount of electric current needed from a circuit to a generator.

■ demand factor

for an electrical system or feeder circuit, this is a ratio of the amount of connected load (in kva or amperes) that will be operating at the same time to the total amount of connected load on the circuit. An 80% demand factor, for instance, indicates that only 80% of the connected load on a circuit will ever be operating at the same time. Conductor capacity can be based on that amount of load.

■ Demand-Side Management (DSM)

DSM is the management of the demand for power. It consists of actions undertaken by utilities to influence consumer use of electricity for the benefit of both the consumer and the utility company. For example, when a utility reaches the point that more capacity is needed, it can either supply more power or reduce demand for electricity through DSM. DSM can include the shifting of demand to off-peak hours, reducing overall consumption, or increasing consumers' overall energy efficiency. Many spread their fixed cost over a specified consumer base, and increase efficiency through economies of scale and load diversity. In return for this franchise, utilities have an 'obligation to serve' all consumers in that territory on demand. This means that utilities must ensure that there are sufficient generation, transmission and distribution systems to serve all their present and future consumers.

■ demarcation point

the point at which operational control changes (for example, where the phone company's responsibility ends and the building owner's begins).

■ demodulation

opposite of modulation, the process of retrieving data from a modulated carrier wave.

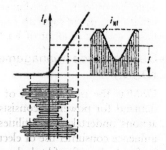

■ density

mass per unit of volume of a substance. i.e.: grams/cu.cm. or pounds/cu.ft.

■ derating

for a DC-DC converter, the specified reduction in output power required for operation at elevated temperatures. The most common operating temperature range specified. Also see **convection cooled**.

■ derivative

the derivative function senses the rate of rise or fall of the system temperature and automatically adjusts the cycle time of the controller to minimise overshoot or undershoot.

■ design life

the expected lifetime of a power supply during which it will operate to its published specifications.

■ destination

the equipment connected to the output of a routing switcher, crosspoint switch or switching array. Used when defining the size of a switching array, the user must specify how many sources and destination there are in the system.

■ detectability

a dynamical system is detectable if all of its unstable modes are observable. Also see **the dual concept of stabilisability**.

■ deviation

the amount by which a quantity differs from its nominal value. For our purposes, the amount by which a frequency differs from the nominal or specified frequency.

■ device

a peripheral which connects to the computer. Mice, keyboards, printers, data acquisition instruments, modules and cards are all devices.

■ dew point

the temperature at which a condensible component of a gas starts to condense into a liquid.

■ dial up

a type of communication that is established by a switched-circuit connection using the telephone network.

■ diaphragm

the sensing element consisting of a membrane which is deformed by the pressure differential applied across it.

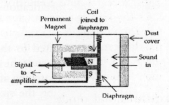

■ dielectric

material used to prevent two points in a electrical circuit from becoming conductively connected. Sometimes called a dielectric barrier.

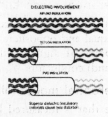

■ dielectric constant

related to the force of attraction between two opposite charges separated by a distance in a uniform medium.

■ dielectric constant (k)

the property of the dielectric material that determines how much electric energy can be stored in a capacitor of a particular size by a value of applied voltage.

■ dielectric strength

the ability of a dielectric material of specified thickness to withstand high voltages without breaking down.

■ dielectric strength - electric strength

the two most important, basic, and unique features that signal-isolation transformers provide are balance and physical separation, i.e. a dielectric barrier. The physical separation of the primary and secondary windings (or line-side and chip-side windings) allows sensitive low-voltage circuits to be safely electromagnetically connected to circuit nodes exposed to high voltage potentials without a direct conductive path. The voltage rating of a transformer is called out by its dielectric strength level in VACRMS or VDC. The transformer is guaranteed to isolate the primary and secondary windings from high-voltage transients below this rated level. The typical dielectric level for most telecom applications is 1500VACRMS for a one minute duration. At some voltage potential, a leakage current will begin to flow through the protective insulation. When the magnitude of this current exceeds a predefined level (typically 500μA), Insulation Breakdown or Dielectric Breakdown is said to have occurred. As per UL1950 (5.3.2): 'Insulation breakdown is considered to have occurred when the current which flows as a result of the application of the test voltage rapidly increases in an uncontrolled manner, i.e. the insulation does not restrict the flow of the current. Corona discharge or a single momentary flashover is not regarded as insulation breakdown.'

■ **dielectric withstand voltage**

the voltage level at which the dielectric breaks down, allowing conduction between isolated conductors or between a conductor and the core. Isolation, or is the ability of a transformer to withstand a specific breakdown voltage between the primary and secondary windings.

■ **differential**

for an on/off controller, it refers to the temperature difference between the temperature at which the controller turns heat off and the temperature at which the heat is turned back on. It is expressed in degrees.

■ **differential amplifier**

one whose output is proportional to the difference between two inputs.

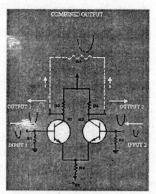

■ **differential gain**

unwanted variations in a video signal's chrominance subcarrier's

amplitude that result from changes in the signal's DC level, usually specified between 10% and 90% of full scale. Expressed in a percentage, or a fraction of a percentage.

■ **differential inputs**

using differential inputs can reduce noise picked up by the signal leads. For each input signal there are two signal wires. A third connector allows the signals to be referenced to ground. The measurement is the difference in voltage between the two wires: any voltage common to both wires is removed.

■ **differential mode**

a current conduction mode in which currents, relative to two conductors, are flowing 180° out of phase, with equal magnitude within the conductors.

■ **differential mode current**

the intended signal currents that are equal and oppositely directed on pairs of signal and return (ground) conductors.

■ **differential mode noise**

noise that is measured between two lines with respect to a common reference point excluding common-mode noise. The resultant measurement is the difference of the noise components of the two lines. The noise between the DC output and DC return is usually measured in power supplies.

■ **differential mode voltage**

the voltage that drives equal and oppositely directed currents to achieve an intended circuit function. The source of differential mode current.

■ **differential output**

an output circuit where the output voltage appears between two active output terminals rather than between one terminal and ground. Normally associated with balanced circuitry. See **differential input**.

■ **differential phase**

unwanted variations in a subcarrier's phase as a result of changes in the chrominance signal's DC level, usually specified between 10% and 90% of full scale. Expressed in degrees, or fractions or a degree.

■ **differential pressure**

the difference in static pressure between two identical pressure taps at the same elevation located in two different locations in a primary device.

■ **digit**

a measure of the display span of a panel meter. By convention, a full digit can assume any value from 0 through 9, a 1/2-digit will display a 1 and overload at 2, a 3/4-digit will display digits up to 3 and overload at 4, etc. For example, a meter with a display span of ±3999 counts is said to be a 3-3/4 digit meter.

■ **digital output**

an output signal which represents the size of an input in the form of a series of discrete quantities.

■ **digital signal 0 (ds-0)**

north American Digital Hierarchy signaling standard for transmission at 64 kbps. (2) Digital Signal Level 0 is the worldwide standard transmission rate (64 kbps) for PCM digitized voice channels. 24 DSOs exist in each DSI (T1) signal.

■ **digital signal 1 (ds-1)**

north American Digital Hierarchy signaling standard for transmission sat 2.544 Mbps. Supports 24 simultaneous DS-O signals. Term often used interchangeably with T-1, although DS-1 signals may be exchanged over other transmission systems.

■ **digital signals**

Data presented as discrete values i.e. On/Off or Binary.

■ **digital-to-analog converter (d/a or dac)**

a device or circuit to convert a digital value to an analog signal level.

■ **diode**

any two-electrode device that conducts in only one direction.

DIODE

P-TYPE	N-TYPE
+	−
Hole	Electron

No current flows
across this junction

Battery

■ **direct access**

the ability of customers to buy

electricity generation directly from power producers or through power marketers.

direct current (dc)

electricity that flows continuously in one direct. (See **alternating current**)

direction discriminator

part of a bi-directional counter which determines the counting direction.

disable

the act of de-asserting the enable signal to turn off the device. In the case of an EN low device, the EN signal must fall below the typical threshold voltage of 1.5V.

disaccommodation

the proportional decrease of permeability after a disturbance of a magnetic material, measured at a constant temperature, over a given time interval. The resultant permeability after magnetic conditioning divided by the permeability of the first measurement times log10 of the ratio of time interval.

discharge time constant

the time required for the output-voltage from a sensor or system to discharge 37% of its original value in response to a zero rise time step function input. This parameter determines a low frequency response.

discharged

the removal of the charge in a capacitor by completing a circuit between the plates.

disconnect

to remove an electrical device from a circuit to make it inoperative.

discrete air gap

mechanical air gap created by a small number of breaks in the magnetic path. In a standard C-core this number is generally two, a standard E-core is generally three, etc.

d-ISDN

broadband Integrated Services Digital Network

disk operating system (DOS)

Program used to control the transfer of information to and from a disk, such as MS DOS.

displacement

The measured distance traveled by a point from its position at rest. Peak to peak displacement is the total measured movement of a vibrating point between its positive and negative extremes. Measurement units expressed as inches or millinches.

displacement current

the current flows in a circuit containing a capacitor whenever the capacitor charges or discharges.

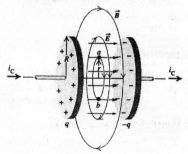

■ dissipation constant

the ratio for a thermistor which relates a change in internal power dissipation to a resultant change of body temperature.

■ dissociation constant (k)

a value which quantitatively expresses the extent to which a substance dissociates in solution. The smaller the value of K, the less dissociation of the species in solution. This value varies with temperature, ionic strength, and the nature of the solvent.

■ distance-coded reference marks

incremental measuring method, whereby the absolute position can be determined by evaluating the systematically varying distances between consecutive reference marks.

■ distortion

any deviation from the mathematical ideal of a real-world periodic waveform, which is specified as a percent of the desired signal. Distortion can be expressed mathematically in terms of the harmonics of the fundamental frequency. This parameter is of considerable importance in instrumentation transformers.

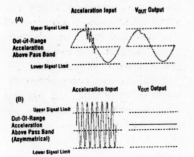

■ distributed air gap

a major feature of iron powder cores. It is the cumulative effect of many small gaps distributed evenly throughout the core. In a typical MPP core, the number of separate air gaps results from the use of powder to construct the core and numbers in the millions. The result is minimal fringing flux density compared to a core with one or two discrete air gaps in the magnetic path.

■ distributed capacitance

in the construction of an inductor, each turn of wire or conductor acts as a capacitor plate. The combined effects of each turn can be presented as a single capacitance known as the distributed capacitance. The capacitance is in parallel with the inductor. This parallel combination will resonate at some frequency, which is called the self-resonant frequency (SRF). Lower distributed capacitance for a given inductance will result in a higher SRF and vice versa.

■ distributed power

system level architecture in which converters operating from a central power bus provide localized power (and various voltage levels) to individual subassemblies/components. The type of power distribution system used is highly dependent upon the needs of a particular application.

■ distribution

a system of delivering acceptable voltage electricity from transmission lines to individual customers.

■ **distribution system**

the whole circuit (system or distribution lines) and all of its branches which supply electricity to consumers.

■ **disturbance rejection**

refers to the ability of a feedback system to attenuate (or reject) disturbances. Typically, it is desirable for feedback systems to attenuate/reject low frequency disturbances.

■ **dlc**

Digital Loop Carrier

■ **DLEC**

Digital Local Carrier

■ **DMA**

acronym Direct memory access. A high speed data storage mode of the IBM PC.

■ **DMT**

discrete Multitone. In DMT, a large number of low-rate carrier frequencies are QAM-modulated at a low rate to transmit a single high-rate data stream. DMT is used for ADSL and proposed for VDSL.

■ **DOCSIS**

data Over Cable System Interface Specification

■ **donor**

a type of impurity that adds electrons to the atoms of a semiconductor substance.

■ **double precision**

the degree of accuracy that requires two computer words to represent a number. Numbers are stored with 17 digits of accuracy and printed with up to 16 digits.

■ **down guy**

a guy wire attached directly from a pole or structure to an anchor rod buried in the ground.

■ **drawing**

the mechanical process of making conductors smaller by forcing through dies.

■ **drift**

slow variation of a performance characteristic such as gain, frequency or power output. May be due to, for instance, temperature or ageing. Usually only significant when measuring low-level signals (a few millivolts) over long periods of time, or in difficult environmental conditions.

■ **drip-loop**

connection point between Edison service wires and customer wiring.

■ **drip-proof guarded**

a drip-proof machine with ventilating openings guarded (with screens) as in a guarded motor.

■ **drip-proof motor**

an open motor in which the ventilating openings are so constructed that drops of liquid or solid particles falling on it, at any angle not greater than 15 degrees from the vertical, cannot enter either directly or by striking and running along a horizontal or inwardly inclined surface.

■ drive level

the amount of power dissipated by the oscillating crystal unit. Usually expressed in terms of mW.

■ driver

a program that controls a device. Each device has its own set of commands that its driver understands, and can translate for other software like Windmill's Logger and Chart.

■ droop

a common occurrence in time-proportional controllers. It refers to the difference in temperature between the set point and where the system temperature actually stabilises due to the time-proportioning action of the controller.

■ drop

slang term used for each cabling span pulled from a telecommunications closet.

■ drop cable

a cable that connects a network device such as a computer to a physical medium such as an Ethernet network. Drop cable is also called transceiver cable because it runs from the network node to a transceiver (a transmit/receiver) attached to the trunk cable.

■ dropout

the lower limit of the AC input voltage where the power supply just begins to experience insufficient input to maintain regulation. The dropout voltage for linears is quite load dependent. For most switchers it is largely design dependent, and to a smaller degree load dependent.

■ dry circuit switching

switching below specified levels of voltage and current to minimise any physical and electrical changes in the contact junction.

■ dry reed relay

a glass enclosed, hermetically sealed, magnetically actuated contact. No mercury or other wetting material is used. Typical atmosphere inside the glass enclosure is nitrogen.

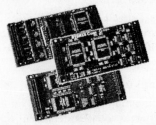

■ DSL

digital Subscriber Line- another name for an ISDN BRI channel. Operated at the Basic Rate Interface (with two 64 kbps circuit switched channels and one 16 kbps packet switched channel), the DSL can carry both voice and data signal at the same time, in both directions, as well as the signaling data used for call information and customer data.

■ DSLAM

digital Subscriber Line access multiplexer

■ DSP

digital Signal Processor- The processing of signal transmission using digital techniques.

■ d-subminiature

a common connector type that

utilises multiple pins and a D shaped housing. Also called D-sub.

■ DTE

DTE stands for Data Terminal Equipment. It is part of the RS232 standard and represents, for example, the PC.

■ dual element sensor

a sensor assembly with two independent sensing elements.

■ dual torque

dual speed motor whose torque varies with speed (as the speed changes the horsepower remains constant).

■ dual voltage

some motors can operate on two different voltages, depending upon how it is built and connected. The voltages are either multiples of two or the 3 of one another.

■ duality

refers to the fact that controllability and observability are dual concepts. The pair (A,B) is controllable if and only if the pair (A^H, B^H) is observable. The pair (A,C) is observable if and only if the pair (A^H, C^H) is controllable. Similarly, stabilisability and detectability are dual concepts.

■ dual-slope a/d converter

an analog-to-digital converter which integrates the signal for a specific time, then counts time intervals for a reference voltage to bring the integrated signal back to zero. Such converters provide high resolution at low cost, excellent

normal-mode noise rejection, and minimal dependence on circuit elements.

■ duplex

pertaining to simultaneous two-way independent data communication transmission in both direction. Same as 'full duplex'.

■ duplex wire

a pair of wires insulated from each other and with an outer jacket of insulation around the inner insulated pair.

■ dustproof

constructed or protected so that dust will not interfere with its successful operation.

■ dusttight

constructed so that dust will not enter the enclosing case under specified test conditions.

■ DUT

abbreviation for Device Under Test. See **UUT**.

■ duty cycle

the relationship between the operating and rest times or repeatable operation at different loads. A motor which can continue to operate within the temperature limits of its insulation system, after it has reached normal operating (equilibrium) temperature is considered to have a continuous duty (CONT.) rating. One which never reaches equilibrium temperature, but is permitted to cool down between operations is operating under intermittent duty (INT.) conditions such as a crane and hoist motor which are often rated 15 or 30 min. duty.

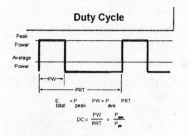

Duty Cycle

$$E_{total} = P_{peak} \quad PW = P_{ave} \quad PRT$$

$$DC = \frac{PW}{PRT} = \frac{P_{ave}}{P_{pk}}$$

■ duty, continuous

a service requirement that demands operation at a substantially constant load for an indefinitely long time.

■ duty, intermittent

a service requirement that demands operation for alternate intervals of load and no load, load and rest, or load, no load, and rest.

■ duty, periodic

a type of intermittent duty in which the load conditions regularly reoccur.

■ duty, short time

a requirement of service that demands operations at a substantially constant load for a short and definitely specified time.

■ duty, varying

a requirement of service that demands operation at loads, and for intervals of time, both of which may be subject to wide variation.

■ DWDM

dense Wavelength Division Multiplexing

■ dynamic (two-plane) balancing machine

a dynamic balancing machine is a centrifugal balancing machine that furnishes information for performing two-plane balancing.

■ dynamic calibration

calibration in which the input varies over a specific length of time and the output is recorded vs. time.

■ dynamic data exchange

a standard Microsoft Windows protocol that defines a way for Windows applications to share information with one another.

■ dynamic load

output load that changes rapidly. Normally specified as both a load change value and a rate of change.

■ dynamic pressure

the difference in pressure levels from static pressure to stagnation pressure caused by an increase in velocity. Dynamic pressure increases by the square of the velocity.

■ dynamic response

output overshoot that occurs when the converter output load is turned on/off or abruptly changed. This overshoot gives the high frequency output impedance of the converter. Also see **output impedance**.

■ dynamic scanning

scanning method by which two alternating signals of constant amplitude and slightly different frequencies are generated and where the phase between the two signals represents the measuring value.

■ dynamic unbalance

dynamic unbalance is that condition in which the central principal axis is not coincident with the shaft axis.

■ dynamometer

a device which loads the motor to measure output torque and speed accurately by providing a calibrated dynamic load. Helpful in testing motors for nameplate information and an effective device in measuring efficiency.

Dynamometer

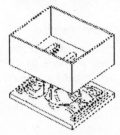

■ e

an electrical symbol for volts.

■ e1

the term for a digital facility used for transmitting data over a telephone network at 2.048 Mbps. The European equivalent of T1.

■ e3

the highest transmission rate generally available in the European digital infrastructure (34 Mbps).

■ eccentricity error

measuring error of an angle encoder caused by an eccentricity in the mounting of the circular graduation.

■ echo

to reflect received data to the sender. For example, keys depressed on a keyboard are usually echoed as characters displayed on the screen.

■ echo cancellation

process by which a transmitter/receiver cancels out the transmitted signal as to 'hear' the received signal better.

■ ECL

the abbreviation for 'Emitter Coupled Logic.'

■ ECL logic

abbreviation for Emitter Coupled Logic, a very high speed digital technology.

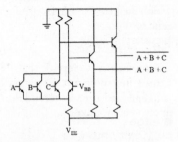

■ ecology

study of the relationship among organisms and the environments in which they live, including all living and nonliving components.

■ eddy current

circulating current produced in

connecting materials by a varying magnetic field. Eddy currents are undesirable in the core of a transformer.

eddy current losses

core losses associated with the electrical resistivity of the magnetic material and induced voltages within the material. Eddy currents are inversely proportional to material resistivity and proportional to the rate of change of flux density. Eddy current losses are present in both the magnetic core and windings of an inductor. Eddy currents in the winding, or conductor, contribute to two main types of losses: losses due to proximity effects and skin effects. As for the core losses, an electric field around the flux lines in the magnetic field is generated by alternating magnetic flux. This will result in eddy currents if the magnetic core material has electrical conductivity. Losses result from this phenomenon since the eddy currents flow in a plane that is perpendicular to the magnetic flux lines. Eddy current and hysteresis losses are the two major core loss factors. Eddy current loss becomes dominant in powder cores as the frequency increases.

edge

enhanced Data rates for Global Evolution

effective area

for a magnetic core of a given geometry, the magnetic cross-sectional area that a hypothetical toroidal core of the same material properties would possess to be the magnetic equivalent to the given core.

effective length (le)

for a magnetic core of a given geometry, the magnetic length that a hypothetical toroidal core of the same material properties would possess to be the magnetic equivalent to the given core.

effective permeability (μe)

for a magnetic circuit constructed with an air gap, or gaps, the permeability of a hypothetical homogeneous material that would provide the same reluctance, or net permeability.

effective value

the value of an alternating current that produces the same heating effect in a pure resistance as a corresponding value of dc. The effective value of a sine curve is equal to .707 times its peak value. Also called ROOT MEANS SQUARED (RMS) VALUE.

effective volume (ve)

for a magnetic core of a given geometry, the magnetic volume that a hypothetical toroidal core of the same material properties would possess to be the magnetic equivalent to the given core.

efficiency

the efficiency of a motor is the ratio of mechanical output to electrical input. It represents the effectiveness with which the motor converts electrical energy into mechanical energy. NEMA has set up codes which correlate to specific nominal efficiencies. A decrease in losses (the elements keeping the motor from being 100% efficient of 10% constitutes an upward improvement of the motor of one code on the NEMA table. Each nominal efficiency has a corresponding minimum efficiency number.

■ EIA

electronic Industries Association.

■ electric current

the flow of electronically charged particles through a conducting circuit due to the presence of a potential difference. The current at any point in a circuit is the amount of charge flowing per second; its SI unit is the ampere (coulomb per second)

■ electric field

a field of force that exists between positively and negatively charged surfaces. In a capacitor, the field is assumed to consist of lines of force which extend through the dielectric from the positive to the negative plate.

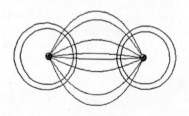

■ electrical codes

rules and regulations for the installation and operation of electrical devices and currents which

state the minimum safety conditions.

■ electrical degree

a unit of measurement of time as applied to alternating current. One complete cycle =360 electrical degrees. One cycle in a rotating electric machine is accomplished when the rotating field moves from one pole to the next pole of the same polarity. There are 360 electrical degrees in this time period. Therefore, in a two pole machine there are 360 degrees in one revolution, and the electrical and mechanical degrees are equal. In a machine with more than two poles, the number of electrical degrees per revolution is obtained by multiplying the number of pairs of poles by 360.

■ electrical interference

electrical noise induced upon the signal wires that obscures the wanted information signal.

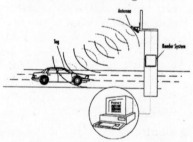

■ electrical time constant (for dc motors)

the ratio of electrical inductance to armature resistance. Electrical time constant in seconds defined as Electrical

$$T/C = (L_a \times l_a) / \text{(hot IR voltage drop)}$$

where L_a is the armature circuit inductance in henries and l_a is the rated full load armature current.

■ electrical unbalance

in a 3 phase supply, where the voltages of the three different phases are not exactly the same. Measured in % of unbalance.

■ electricity

all phenomena caused by electric charge, whether static or in motion. Electric charge is caused by an excess or deficit of electrons in the charged substance, and an electric current by the movement of electrons around a circuit. Substances may be electrical conductors, such as metals, which allow the passage of electricity through them, or insulators, such as rubber, which are extremely poor conductors.

■ electrode

an element of an electron tube or semiconductor device that takes part in conduction, such as the plate, anode, cathode and filament.

■ electrode potential (e)

the difference in potential established between an electrode and a solution when the electrode is immersed in the solution.

■ electrodynamics

the branch of physics dealing with electric currents and associated magnetic forces. Quantum electrodynamics (QED) studies the interaction between charged particles and their emission and absorption of electromagnetic radiation. This field combines quantum theory and relatively theory, making accurate predictions about subatomic processes involving charged particles such as electrons and protons.

■ electrolyte

any substance which, when in solution will conduct an electric current. Acids, bases, and salts are common electrolytes.

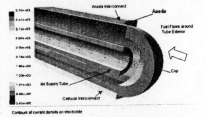

■ electromagnetic induction

the process of developing a voltage in a wire that is being either cut by or is cutting a magnetic field.

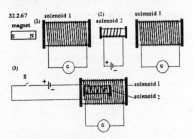

■ electromagnetic interference (EMI)

unwanted electrical or electromagnetic energy that causes unwanted responses in electronic equipment.

■ electromagnetic waves

oscillating electric and magnetic fields traveling together through space at a speed of nearly 186,000 mi/300,000 km per second. The (limitless) range of possible wavelengths or frequencies or electromagnetic waves, which can be thought of as making up the electromagnetic spectrum, includes radio waves, infrared radiation, visible light, ultraviolet radiation, X-rays and gamma rays.

■ electromechanical effects

a relay that uses an electromagnet to move an armature thereby actuating current.

■ electromotive force (EMF)

the potential difference between the two electrodes in a cell. The cell emf is the cell voltage measured when no current is flowing through the cell. It can be measured by means of a pH meter with high input impedance.

■ electron emmission

the escape of electrons from certain materials.

■ electron microscope

instrument that produces a magnified image by using a beam of electronics instead of light rays, as in a optical microscope. An electron lens is an arrangement of electromagnetic coils that control and focus the beam. Electrons are not visible to the eye, so instead of an eyepiece there is a fluorescent screen or photographic plate on which the electrons form an image. The wavelength of the electron beam is much shorter than that of light, so much greater magnification and resolution (ability to distinguish detail) can be achieved. The development of the

electron microscope has made possible the observation of very minute organisms, viruses and even large molecules.

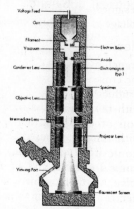

■ electron tube

an arrangement of two or more conductive elements, enclosed in an envelope, to control electron flow in a circuit.

■ electronic industries association

a standards organisation specialising in the electrical and functional characteristics of interface equipment.

■ electronic load

an electronic device designed to provide a load to the outputs of a power supply, usually capable of dynamic loading, and frequently programmable or computer controlled.

■ electronic low-voltage

electronic low-voltage lighting uses an electronic (solid-state technology) transformer to convert normal line voltage (120 VAC) to low voltage (typically 12 VAC). This lower voltage is then used power an incandescent low-voltage lamp. Only use a dimmer specifically designed for an electronic low-voltage transformer.

■ electronics

branch of science that deals with the emission of electronics from conductors and semiconductors, with the subsequent manipulation of these electronics, and with the construction of electronic devices. The first electronic device was the thermionic valve, or vacuum tube, in which electrons moved in a vacuum, and led to such inventions as radio, television, radar and the digital computer. Replacement of valves with the comparatively tiny and reliable transistor in 1948 revolutionised electronic development. Modern electronic devices are based on minute integrated circuits (silicon chips), wafer-thin crystal slices holding tens of thousands of electronic components).

■ electrostatic discharge (ESD)

current produced by two objects having a static charge when they are brought close enough to produce an arc or discharge.

■ electrostatic shield

see **faraday shield**.

■ element

any of the electrical parts of an electron tube such as the filament, cathode or plate.

■ embodied energy

it takes energy to make something. Embodied energy is associated with the production of a good or service or the energy to prepare or make a product. Using french fries as an example, substantial energy is embodied in the planting, cultivation and harvesting of the potatoes. Then energy is used in the preparation of the French fries' packaging, transportation, marketing, storing, cooking and service to a hungry teenager. Embodied energy can be reduced by limiting food processing, or by recycling.

■ EMF

Electromotive force. A rise in (electrical) potential energy. The principal unit is the volt.

■ EMI

abbreviation for Electromagnetic Interference. A term that defines unwanted electromagnetic radiation from a device which could interfere with desired signals in test or communication equipment. RFI (Radio Frequency Interference) and EMI are often used interchangeably.

■ emi filter

filter placed at the input to an off-line converter that minimises the effect of EMI on the converter and the associated system.

■ emissivity

the ratio of energy emitted by an object to the energy emitted by a blackbody at the same temperature. The emissivity of an object depends upon its material and surface texture; a polished metal surface can have an emissivity around 0.2 and a piece of wood can have an emissivity around 0.95.

■ **enable**

the act of asserting the enable signal to turn on the device. In the case of an EN low device, the EN signal must exceed the typical threshold voltage of 1.5V Synonyms: EN

■ **enable high/low**

some USB controller ships have enable logic that requires the power switch to be active low while others require the switch to be active high. This signal will be connected to the enable pin of the device selected.

■ **enable/disable function**

a control function that enables or disables the output of the oscillator. When the oscillator is in its disabled state, the oscillator is still running internally, but no output is coming from the output pin.

■ **enable/disable time**

the time between application of the proper voltage to the enable/disable pin and the moment the output becomes enabled or disabled.

■ **encapsulated winding**

a motor which has its winding structure completely coated with an insulating resin (such as epoxy). This construction type is designed for exposure to more severe atmospheric conditions than the normal varnished winding.

■ **enclosures**

the housing, frame, of the motor of which there are two broad classifications; open and totally closed. There are specific types of each:

■ **encoder**

apparatus consisting of a measuring standard and a scanning unit (transducer, sensor).

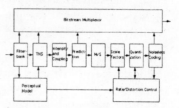

■ **end point (potentiometric)**

the apparent equivalence point of a titration at which a relatively large potential change is observed.

■ **end points**

the end points of a full scale calibration curve.

■ **endothermic**

absorbs heat. A process is said to be endothermic when it absorbs heat.

■ **endurance limit**

in fatigue testing, the number of cycles which may be withstood without failure at a particular level of stress.

■ **energy**

capacity for doing work. Potential energy (PE) is energy deriving from position; thus a stretched spring has elastic PE, and an object raised to a height above the Earth's surface, or the water in an elevated reservoir, has gravitational PE. A lump of coal and a tank of gasoline, together with the oxygen needed for their combination, have chemical energy. Other sorts of energy include electrical and nuclear energy, and light and sound. Moving bodies possess kinetic energy (KE). Energy can be converted from one form to another, but the total quantity stays the same (in accordance with the conservation of energy principle). For example, as an apple falls, it loses gravitational PE but gains KE. Although energy is never lost, after a number of conversions it tends to finish up as the kinetic energy of random motion of molecules (of the air, for example) at relatively low temperatures. This is "degraded" energy in that it is difficult to convert it back to other forms.

■ **energy conservation**

methods of reducing energy use through insulation, increasing energy efficiency, and changes in patterns of use. Profligate energy use by industrialized countries contributes greatly to air pollution and the greenhouse effect when it draws on nonrenewable energy sources.

■ **energy storage**

the amount of magnetic energy which can be stored in a given inductor in microjoules. It is the product of one half the inductance required in microhenries (μH) and the current (I) squared in amperes.

■ **energy storage inductors**

inductors used for energy storage, generally in power conversion rather than filtering or tuning.

■ **enterprise network**

a large typical corporate network under the auspices of one organisation.

■ **enthalpy**

the sum of the internal energy of a body and the product of its volume multiplied by the pressure.

■ **environment**

scottish historian and essayist, Thomas Carlyle, introduced the word 'environment' in the 19th century to define our surroundings. In the 17th century, 'environs' meant your neighborhood. Today, your 'neighborhood' has reached global proportions, so much so that technology and energy consumption far removed from our community can alter the vitality of our atmosphere, ocean and land.

■ **environmental conditions**

all conditions in which a transducer may be exposed during shipping, storage, handling, and operation.

■ **EPROM**

Erasable Programmable Read-Only Memory. The PROM can be erased by ultraviolet light or electricity.

DIP

V_{PP}	1		28	V_{CC}
A12	2		27	A14
A7	3		26	A13
A6	4		25	A8
A5	5		24	A9
A4	6		23	A11
A3	7		22	OE# (G#)
A2	8		21	A10
A1	9		20	CE# (E#)
A0	10		19	DQ7
DQ0	11		18	DQ6
DQ1	12		17	DQ5
DQ2	13		16	DQ4
V_{SS}	14		15	DQ3

■ equalisation

selective amplification (signal restoration) applied to a signal in order to compensate for high frequency attenuation and other distortions encountered in long lengths of cable.

■ equilibrium constant

the product of the concentrations (or activities) of the substances produced at equilibrium in a chemical reaction divided by the product of concentrations of the reacting substances, each concentration raised to that power which is the coefficient of the substance in the chemical equation.

■ equipment room

the space dedicated to telecommunications equipment.

■ equitransference

equal diffusion rates of the positively and negatively charged ions of an electrolyte across a liquid junction without charge separation.

■ equivalent circuit

the equivalent circuit shown below depicts electrical activity of a quartz crystal unit operating at its natural resonant frequency. The C_O, or shunt capacitance, represents the capacitance of the crystal electrodes plus the capacitance of the holder and leads. R_1, C_1, and L_1 compose the "motional arm" of the crystal, and are referred to as the motional parameters. The motional inductance (L_1) represents the vibrating mass of

the crystal unit. The motional capacitance (C_1) represents the elasticity of the quartz, and the resistance (R_1), represents bulk losses occurring within the quartz.

Simplified equivalent circuit of a Quartz Crystal

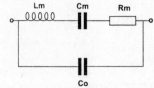

■ equivalent conductance (l)

equivalent conductance of an electrolyte is defined as the conductance of a volume of solution containing one equivalent weight of dissolved substances when placed between two parallel electrodes 1 cm apart, and large enough to contain between them all of the solution. l is never determined directly, but is calculated from the specific conductance (Ls). If C is the concentration of a solution in gram equivalents per liter, then the concentration of a solution in gram equivalents per liter, then the concentration per cubic centimeter is C/1000, and the volume containing one equivalent of the solute, is, therefore, 1000/C.

■ equivalent series inductance (esl)

inductance in series with an 'ideal' capacitor. Sources include leads, terminals, electrodes etc.

■ equivalent series resistance (esr)

resistance in series with an 'ideal'

capacitor. Sources include lead resistance, terminal losses, etc. An important specification for high frequency applications.

■ error

the difference between the value indicated by the transducer and the true value of the measurand being sensed. Usually expressed in percent of full scale output.

■ error amplifier

operational or different amplifier used in the control feedback loop of a converter. The amplifier produces an error voltage when the output (tapped off a voltage divider network) differs from a reference voltage. This error voltage is used to adjust the operation of the PWM so as to correct the sensed output voltage. Sometimes called a Reference Amplifier.

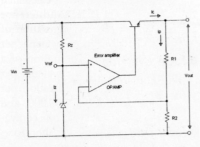

■ error band

the allowable deviations to output from a specific reference norm. Usually expressed as a percentage of full scale.

■ error signal

usually refers to the difference between a desired quantity and the actual quantity. Also see **tracking error**.

■ esp

electric Service Provider. A third party from whom you can purchase Direct Access services, like electricity generation.

■ ESR

1. the abbreviation for 'Equivalent Series Resistance.' As a crystal unit has a resistive element, this term is required in order to define and quantify that characteristic.
2. Equivalent Series Resistance. The value of resistance in series with an ideal capacitor which duplicates the performance characteristics of a real capacitor.

■ etch

a process used in the manufacture of some types of crystal units. The etch process results in an improved surface condition and an increase in the frequency of a blank. The word 'etch' is also used to describe the material used in the etch process, as well as the process itself.

■ ethernet

a baseband LAN specification invented by Xerox Corporation and developed jointly by Xerox, Intel, and Digital Equipment Corporation. Ethernet networks operate at 10 Mbps using CSMA/CD to run over coaxial cable. Ethernet has become a series of standards produced by IEEE referred to as IEEE 802.3.

■ e-type thermocouple

chromel-constantan thermocouple with a temperature range of 0 to 800 °C.

eutectic temperature

the lowest possible melting point of a mixture of alloys.

excitation

the external application of electrical voltage current applied to a transducer for normal operation.

excitation current

the current required to overcome the losses in a core, which begins to produce magnetic energy (or flux) in an inductor.

exothermic

gives off heat. A process is said to be exothermic when it releases heat.

expansion factor

correction factor for the change in density between two pressure measurement areas in a constricted flow.

explosion proof

designed and constructed to withstand and internal explosion without creating an external explosion or fire.

explosion-proof enclosure

an enclosure that can withstand an explosion of gases within it and prevent the explosion of gases surrounding it due to sparks, flashes or the explosion of the container itself, and maintain an external temperature which will not ignite the surrounding gases.

exposed junction

a form of construction of a thermocouple probe where the hot or measuring junction protrudes beyond the sheath material so as to be fully exposed to the medium being measured. This form of construction usually gives the fastest response time.

extended temperature range

an option available on selected oscillators. Extended temperature range is -40°C to +85°C.

externality

these are the unpaid costs and impacts of energy development and use. Externalities from smog include effects upon visibility, health and the destruction of trees. The consequences of externalities can be quite severe, from threatening our national security to possibly affecting the global climate

extrusion

the mechanical process of coating a wire or group of wires with insulating material.

fade override

the ability to temporarily set fade times to zero for all lighting scenes.

fade rate

the time it takes each zone/channel to arrive at the next scene dependent on the degree of change in light level.

fade time

the time it takes all zone/channels to fade from one lighting scene to another with all zones/channels arriving at the next scene at the same time.

■ fahrenheit

a temperature scale defined by 32° at the ice point and 212° at the boiling point of water at sea level.

■ failsafe

in terms of relay technology, when power is lost, the relay contacts fall back to a default position.

■ failure mode

reason for which a converter either does not meet or stops meeting its specified parameters.

■ fall time

the amount of time it takes the output voltage to go from Logic '1' to logic '0'.

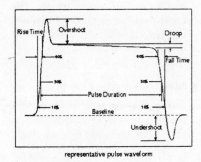

representative pulse waveform

■ fan cooled

see **forced air cooling**.

■ farad

The unit of measure for capacitance. It is the capacitance of a capacitor in which an applied voltage of one volt will store a charge of one coulomb. The more practical units of capacitance are the microfarad and picofarad.

■ faraday shield

electrostatic shield that reduces coupling capacitance in transformers. The shield, which effectively reduces output common mode noise, is placed between the primary and secondary windings of a transformer.

■ fast fourier transfer

an analysis algorithm - given a finite set of data points, the FFT expresses the data in terms of its component frequencies.

■ fault

point of trouble in an electric circuit.

■ fault mode current

input current drawn by a converter when the output is shorted.

■ fault mode input current

the input current to a power supply with a short circuit on the output.

■ fdm

frequency division multiplexing.

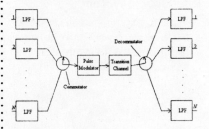

■ fdma

frequency division multiple access

■ feed forward

method of improving line regulation by directly sensing the input voltage of the converter. Also see **line regulation**.

■ feedback

refers to the the use of feedback measurements to enhance the properties of a physical system called the plant. Feedback may be used for any one of the following reasons: (i) stabilisation of an unstable system, (ii) altering the natural modes of a system, (iii) sensitivity reduction to modeling uncertainty, (iv) command following, (v) rejection/attenuation of disturbances, (vi) approximate linearization, and (vii) approximate inversion. It is arguable that uncertaintyin general is the main reason for needing feedback control laws. One, of course, must always be extremely careful when closing a feedback loop. This is because if done improperly the resulting closed loop system may be unstable even if the open loop system is stable. Given this, one must conclude that feedback can be very dangerous!

■ feedback system

refers to a system which uses feedback measurements to enhance the properties of a physical system called the plant.

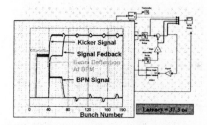

■ feeder

a circuit, such as conductors in conduit or a busway run, which carries a large block of power from the service equipment to a sub-feeder panel or a branch circuit panel or to some point at which the block power is broken into smaller circuits.

■ ferrite core

ferrite is a magnetic material which consists of a mixed oxide of iron and other elements that are made to have a crystalline molecular structure. The crystalline structure is created by firing the ferrite material at a very high temperture for a specified amount of time and temperature profile. The general composition of ferrites is xxFe204 where xx represents one or several metals. The most popular metal combinations are manganese and zinc(MnZn) and nickel and zinc (NiZn). These metals can be easily magnetised.

■ ferrite/ferrite cores

ferrite is a magnetic material that consists of a mixed oxide of iron and other elements that are made to have a crystalline molecular structure. Firing the ferrite material at a very high temperature for a specified amount of time and temperature profile creates the crystalline structure. The general composition of ferrite is xxFe2O4 where xx represents one or several metals. The most popular metal combinations are manganese and zinc (MnZn) and nickel and zinc (NiZn). These materials can be easily magnetised with little coercive force. Available in a variety of shapes and sizes, these ceramic magnetic cores are composed of ferric oxide and a combination of manganese, zinc, or nickel. The shapes EE, PQ, UU, ETD, and dual-slab are used for high frequency power applications. Telecommunications and low power applications use pot cores, touch tone cores, EP, and RM. Slugs, rods, and beads are used for radio frequency applications.

ferromagnetism

ferromagnetic materials have atomic fields that align themselves parallel with externally applied fields creating a total magnetic field much greater than the applied field. Ferromagnetic materials have permeabilities much greater than air (1). Above the curie temperature, the ferromagnetic materials become paramagnetic.

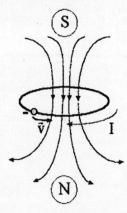

ferroresonant power supply

power supply used at higher power levels in fixed applications, since they are very heavy. Can only be used effectively when the line frequency is very stable as they are sensitive to variations of input AC frequencies.

ferroresonat transformer

transformer in which part of the core is driven in saturation by a resonant tank circuit. The output of the transformer, taken from the saturated portion, is relative immune to variations in input voltage.

ferrule

A compressible tubular fitting that is compressed onto a probe inside a compression fitting to form a gas-tight seal.

FET

Field Effect Transistor, a majority carrier voltage controlled transistor.

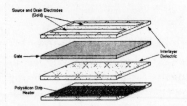

fiber distributed data interface

a 100Mbps fiber optic cabling standard developed by ANSI. FDDI utilises a dual counter rotating ring topology for network redundancy.

fiber optic cable

a transmission medium that uses glass or plastic fibers, rather than copper wire, to transport data or voice signals. The signals is imposed on the fiber via pulses (modulation) of light from a laser or a light-emitting diode (LED). Because of its high bandwidth and lack of susceptibility to interference, fiber-optic cable is used in long-haul or noisy applications.

fiber optics

a method for the transmission of information (sound, pictures, data). Light is modulated and transmitted over high purity, hair-thin fibers of glass. The bandwidth capacity of fiber optic cable is much greater than that of conventional cable or copper wire.

field

the windings of an electric generator which are supplied with dc to produce the steady electromagnetic field. Generators used for demonstration purposes may use permanent magnets to produce the magnetic field.

field balancing equipment

an assembly of measuring instruments for performing balancing operations on assembled machinery which is not mounted in a balancing machine.

field of view

A volume in space defined by an angular cone extending from the focal plane of an instrument.

field strength (h)

the parameter characterising the amplitude of AC or DC field strength. The magnitude of current, number of turns, and winding geometry determine field strength.

field weakening

the introduction of resistance in series with the shunt wound field of a DC motor to reduce the voltage and current which weakens the strength of the magnetic field and thereby increases the motor speed.

fifo buffer

a first in, first out, store. The first value placed in the buffer (queue) is the first value subsequently read.

filament

In a directly heated electron tube, a heating element which also serves as the emitter.

file

a set of related records or data treated as a unit.

filling solution

a solution of defined composition to make contact between an internal element and a membrane or sample. The solution sealed inside a pH glass bulb is called an internal filling solution. This solution normally contains a buffered chloride solution to provide a stable potential and a designated zero potential point. The solution which surrounds the reference electrode internal and periodically requires replenishing is called the reference filling solution. It provides contact between the reference electrode internal and sample through a junction.

filter

a circuit or device whose purpose is to control electrical energy at a given frequency or over a range of frequencies. Groups of passive components are commonly used to construct many types of fileters. These passive components include resistors, capacitors and inductors.

filtering

attenuates components of a signal that are undesired: reduces noise errors in a signal.

firmware

Programs stored in PROMs.

first law of thermodynamics

the First Law of Thermodynamics is simply a statement of the conservation of energy. Energy can be neither created nor destroyed, only transformed. No matter which form it takes, the total energy in the system is a constant.

fission

in 1939, exiled German physicist Lise Meitner theorized that when a neutron hits a uranium nucleus, it splits the nucleus into two parts. She was soon proven correct and the reaction was called 'fission' from the Latin word 'fission' meaning 'to split.' The process releases large amounts of energy that can be used to boil water, create steam, turn a generator and generate electricity.

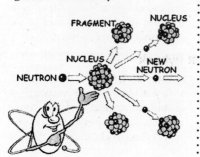

flag

any of various types of indicators used for identification of a condition or event; for example, a character that signals the termination of a transmission.

flag delay time

design feature that delays the FLG notification signal in response to an abnormal condition (hot plug event, overcurrent surge, overtemperature condition). This feature minimises unnecessary nuisance tripsÓ caused by the inrush current of high capacitive loads.

flange

mounting endshield with special rabbets and bolt holes for mounting such equipment as pumps and gear boxes to the motor or for overhanging the motor on the driven machine.

flash arc

the flow of electric current across the gap in a circuit which causes a light or a flow.

flatness

a term expressed in dB to specify the consistent amplitude of a signal spanning a frequency range. Typical expressions: Flatness is to be +/-1dB across (frequency range), Or flatness shall have <1.5dB peak to peak.

flexible conduit

nonrigid conduit made of a fabric or metal strip wound spirally.

floating

the condition where a common mode voltage exists, or may exist between earth ground and the instrument or circuit of interest. Low side of circuit is not at earth potential.

floating output

converter output that ungrounded and not referenced to another output. Typically, floating outputs are fully isolated and may be referenced positive or negative by the user. Outputs that are not floating share common return and as such, are referenced to one another.

floppy disk

a small, flexible disk carrying a magnetic medium in which digital data is stored for later retrieval and use.

flow

travel of liquids or gases in response to a force (i.e. pressure or gravity).

flow rate

actual speed or velocity of fluid movement.

flowmeter

a device used for measuring the flow or quantity of a moving fluid.

FLP

Field Labour Provider

fluctuating voltage

service goes from bright to dim and back to bright intermittently.

- **Maximum Deviation (dmax)**
- **Constant Deviation (dc)**
- **-3% Point (dt)**

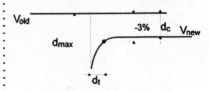

flux

the magnetic field which is established around an energized conductor or permanent magnet. The field is represented by flux lines creating a flux pattern between opposite poles. The density of the flux lines is a measure of the strength of the magnetic field.

flux density (b)

the corresponding parameter for the induced magnetic field in an area perpendicular to the flux path. Flux density is determined by the field strength and permeability of the medium in which it is measured.

flux transfer ratio

the numeric amount of flux intercepted by the secondary winding and the total flux created by the applied ampere-turns.

flyback

actually an isolated storage inductor, a flyback transformer is a combination of an isolating transformer, output inductor, and flywheel diode. These use a gapped core and have a power handling capability of 100VA. Storing energy in the gap when the switch is on and delivering energy to the load when the switch is off, they do not perform like standard transformers.

■ flyback converter

also called a "buck-boost" converter, this topology typically uses

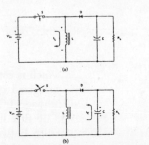

(a)

(b)

FLYBACK COVERTER n/o BUCK-BOOST CONVERTER

a single transistor switch and eliminates the need for an output inductor. Energy is stored in the transformer primary during the first half of the switching period when the transistor switch is on. During the second half or "flyback" period when the transistor is off, this energy is tranferred the transformer secondary and load. Also see Boost Regulator, Buck Regulator, Bridge Converter, Forward Converter, Push-Pull Converter and Resonant Converter.

■ flyback transformer

transformer used in a flyback power supply. Also called horizontal output transformer.

■ fm

Factory Mutual Research Corpo-

ration. An Organisation which sets industrial safety standards.

■ fm approved

an instrument that meets a specific set of specifications established by Factory Mutual Research Corporation.

■ foldback current limiting

converter protection technique in which the circuit is protected under overload conditions by reducing the output current as the load approaches short circuit. This minimised internal power dissipation under short circuit conditions.

■ forced air cooling

use of a fan (or other air moving equipment) within a (sub) system to move air across heat producing components in order to reduce the ambient temperature. Also called forced convection.

■ forced vibration

vibration of a system caused by an imposed force. Steady-state vibration is an unchanging condition of periodic or random motion.

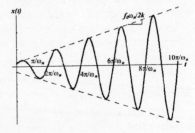

■ form factor

a figure of merit which indicates

how much rectified current departs from pure (non-pulsating) DC. A large departure from unity form factor (pure DC, expressed as 1.0) increases the heating effect of the motor and reduces brush life. Mathematically, form factor is the ratio of the root-mean square (rms) value of the current to the average (av) current or I'ms/Iav.

■ form wound

a type of coil in which each winding is individually formed and placed into the stator slot. A cross sectional view of the winding would be rectangular. Usually form winding is used on high voltage, 2300 volts and above, and large motors (449T and above). Form winding allows for better insulation on high voltage than does random (mush) winding.

■ formation

a formation refers to either a certain layer of the earth's crust, or a certain area of a layer. It often refers to the area of rock where a petroleum reservoir is located.

■ fortran

formula translation language. A widely used high-level programming language well suited to problems that can be expressed in terms of algebraic formulas. It is generally used in scientific applications.

■ forward bias

A dc voltage applied to a PN junction semiconductor so that the positive terminal of the voltage

source connects to the P-type material and the negative terminal to the N-type material. It produces forward current in the circuit.

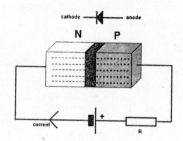

■ forward converter

also called a 'Buck-Derived' converter, this topology, like the flyback converter, typically uses a single transistor switch. Unlike the flyback converter, energy is tranferred to the transformer secondary while the transistor switch is 'on', and stoed in a output inductor. See **boost regulator, buck regulator, bridge converter, flyback converter, push pull converter and resonant converter.**

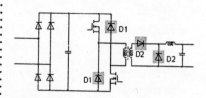

■ forward converter transformer

a transformer which operates by transferring power to the load during the on time and resetting in the off time. Since this transformer only transfers power during half of an input cycle it is required to be larger than a push-pull transformer for example.

■ forward current

current in a circuit of a semiconductor device due to conduction by majority carriers across the PN junction.

■ fossil fuels

stored solar energy in the form of coal, natural gas and oil. They are nonrenewable energy sources from organisms that lived long ago. Upon death, organisms under special conditions were altered chemically and physically. The word fossil is derived from the Latin word "fossilis" from "fodere" meaning "to dig." Today, we use some of that chemically-stored energy to "dig" (mine, drill, trap) for more fossil fuels. Unfortunately, our supply of fossil fuels is becoming depleted. As it is now, the burning of fossil fuels is increasing the concentration of CO_2 and other pollutants, affecting the temperature and chemical reactions in our atmosphere.

■ FPGA

Field-Programmable Gate Array

■ FPM

Flow velocity in feet per minute.

■ FPS

Flow velocity in feet per second.

■ fractional t1

a WAN communications service that provides the user with some portion of a T1 circuit which has been divided into 24 separate 64 kbps channels.

■ fractional-horsepower motor

a motor usually built in a frame smaller than that having a continuous rating of one horsepower, open construction, at 1700 -1800 rpm. Within NEMA frame sizes FHP encompasses the 42, 48 and 56 frames. (In some cases the motor rating does exceed 1 HP, but the frame size categorizes the motor as a fractional.) The height in inches from the centre of the shaft to the bottom of the base can be calculated by dividing the frame size by 16.

■ frame

the supporting structure for the stator parts of an AC motor; in a DC motor the frame usually forms a part of the magnetic coil. The frame also determines mounting dimensions (see **frame size**).

■ frame relay

a streamlined packet switching protocol designed to provide high-speed frame or packet switching with minimal delay and efficient bandwidth usage.

■ frame size

refers to a set of physical dimensions of motors as established by NEMA. These dimensions include critical mounting dimensions. 48 and 56 frame motors are considered fractional horsepower sizes even though they can exceed 1 horsepower, 143T to 449T are considered integral horsepower AC motors and 5000 series and above are called large motors.

■ free convection

operating environment where the natural movement of air (unassisted by fans or blowers) maintains the power module within its operating limits. Also called natural convection.

■ freezing point

The temperature at which the substance goes from the liquid phase to the solid phase.

■ frequency

the periodic repetition of an event within a unit of time. In an electrical circuit, the number of waves that pass a given point in one second. The number of times a resonator plate oscillates or vibrates in one second. The nominal or desired frequency specified by a customer.

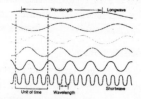

■ frequency counter

counts digital pulses over a defined gate time. A typical gate time is between 0.1 and 10 seconds.

■ frequency modulated output

a transducer output which is obtained in the form of a deviation from a centre frequency, where the deviation is proportional to the applied stimulus.

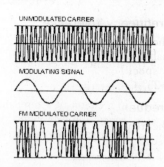

■ frequency of operation

see **switching frequency**

■ frequency of vibration

the number of cycles occurring in a given unit of time. RPM - revolutions per minute. CPM- cycles per minute.

■ frequency output

an output in the form of frequency which varies as a function of the applied input.

■ frequency range

the measure of a circuit's ability to pass a full amplitude signal over a range of signal frequencies. Normally measured between the point or points where the signal amplitude falls to -3dB below the passband frequency. Normally defines the 'bandwidth' of a device or system.

■ frequency response

see **bode plot**.

■ frequency stability

the allowable deviation, in parts per million (PPM), over a specified temperature range. Deviation is referenced to the measured frequency at +25° C.

■ **frequency tolerance**

the allowable deviation from nominal, in parts per million (PPM), at a specific temperature, usually +25° C.

■ **frequency, natural**

the frequency of free (not forced) oscillations of the sensing element of a fully assembled transducer.

■ **fringing fields or fringing flux**

the field(s) associated with the divergence of the flux from the shortest path between poles in a magnetic circuit. Where flux passes through a high permeability into a lower permeability material, the flux redistributes and tends to have a barreling effect between the two poles. See also leakage flux.

■ **front accessible service switch (fass)**

an air-gap switch that can be conveniently activated without removing the wallplate of a control. When switch is turned off, power is completely removed from the device's load circuit by an air-gap switch.

■ **front end of a motor**

the front end of a normal motor is the end opposite the coupling or driving pulley. (NEMA) this is sometimes called the opposite pulley end (O.P.E.) or commutator end (C.E.).

■ **front panel**

the front surface of a unit, generally containing switches and indicator lights.

■ **f-type connector**

a threaded medium performance coaxial signal connector typically used in consumer applications (TV's and VCR's). This connector is typically usable as high as 1GHz. It is inexpensive since the pin of the connector is actually the centre conductor of the coaxial cable.

■ **fuel**

a material used to make heat or power by burning; fuel is a major operating requirement and expense of an electric utility company. Coal oil and natural gas are fossil fuels; fissionable uranium-235 is nuclear fuel.

■ **fuel chain**

the chain of activities involved in transforming energy into forms more convenient for society. This "chain" may include some or all of the following: fuel exploration, extraction, preparation, transportation, conversion to electricity, distribution and waste disposal.

■ **full bridge**

four power switches are used in a full bridge and usually utilise a single primary winding. Full supply voltage is obtained in both directions and utilises the core and windings more effectively. Voltage on the switches does not exceed the supply voltage.

■ **full bridge converter**

converter topology that typically operates as forward converter but uses a bridge circuit, consisting of four switching transistors, to drive the transformer primary. Also see **bridge converter**.

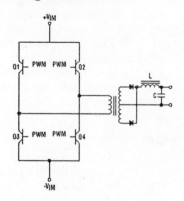

full bridge forward converter

the full bridge is more complex than other switcher topologies. It has the capability for very high performance. It can product high power with four switchers and requires only two magnetic elements.

full fanout

distributing the same signal to multiple destinations.

full load

maximum value of output load specified for a converter under continuous operating conditions.

full load voltage

variations in winding resistance, turns ratio, and leakage can cause minor discrepancies in output voltage, which is the full load voltage.

full scale output

the difference between the minimum output (normally zero) of a data acquisition device and the rated capacity.

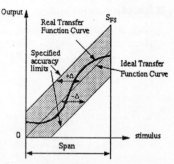

Transfer Function, Span and Full Scale Output

full winding

a winding for toroidal cores that will result in 45% of the cores inside diameter remaining.

full-load current

the current flowing through the line when the motor is operating at full-load torque and full-load speed with rated frequency and voltage applied to the motor terminals.

full-load torque

that torque of a motor necessary to produce its rated horsepower at full-load speed, sometimes referred to as running torque.

full-range dimming

continuous dimming, full intensity to minimum, with no visibly discernable increments in light level.

full-wave rectifier

see **rectification**

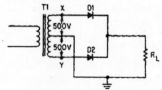

A CONVENTIONAL FULL-WAVE RECTIFIER

■ functions

class of devices designed to perform a specific task. Examples include USB internet cameras, joysticks, mice, and digital cameras.

■ functions

three mode PID controller. A timeproportioning controller with integral and derivative functions. The integral function automatically adjusts the system temperature to the set point temperature to eliminate droop due to the time proportioning function.

■ fundamental

the lowest frequency at which a resonator plate will oscillate. This frequency is determined by the physical dimensions of the plate.

■ fusion

fusion is derived from the Latin word fuses meaning to melt. It involves releasing an enormous amount of energy by joining the nuclei of small atoms. Fusion was considered by scientists as a possible energy source long before fission.

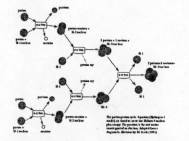

■ fusion splice (fiber optic)

a permanent splice where the two fiber ends are welded together.

■ g

the force of acceleration due to gravity equal to 32.1739 ft/sec^2 or 386 in./sec^2.

■ gain

the amount of amplification used in an electrical circuit.

■ gain margin

the upward gain margin of a feedback system is the amount that the gain of a feedback loop may be increased before going unstable. Upward gain margin is expressed as a fraction which is greater than or equal to unity. The downward gain margin of a feedback system is the amount that the gain of a feedback loop may be reduced before going unstable. Downward gain margin is expressed as a fraction which is less than or equal to unity. See **phase margin** and **delay margin**. Also see **phase cross overs**. Gain margin is by definition measured at phase crossover frequencies.

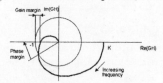

■ galvanometer

an instrument that measures small electrical currents by means of deflecting magnetic coils.

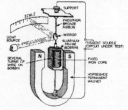

◼ gang

single-gang = one control mounted in a single wallbox.

Multigang = two or more controls mounted side-by-side in a series of connected wallboxes.

◼ ganged control

a method of control that allows the system to control multiple levels of switching with a single command. Such is the case in a video system where different levels are assigned to the different colours in a video signal (R = Red, G = Green and B = Blue). A single command will control all three levels simultaneously.

◼ ganged port protection

protection method where one circuit protection device (or output) is used to protect more than one output port.

◼ gauge factor

a measure of the ratio of the relative change of resistance to the relative change in length of a piezoresistive strain gauge.

◼ gauge length

The distance between two points where the measurement of strain occurs.

◼ gauge pressure

Absolute pressure minus local atmospheric pressure.

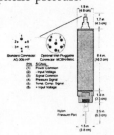

◼ gauge pressure transducer

a transducer which measures pressure in relation to the ambient pressure.

◼ gauss

the CGS unit of measurement for flux density. One Gauss is equal to 1 Maxwell per cm2.

◼ gearhead

the portion of a gearmotor which contains the actual gearing which converts the basic motor speed to the rated output speed.

◼ gearmotor

a gearhead and motor combination to reduce the speed of the motor to obtain the desired RPM's.

◼ general purpose motor

a general-purpose motor is any motor having a "B" design, listed and offered in standard ratings with standard operating characteristics and mechanical construction for use under usual service conditions without restriction to a particular application or type of application. (NEMA)

◼ generation

producing electricity at power plants.

■ generators

machines used to convert mechanical energy into electric energy. They accomplish this by causing one or a series of interconnected coils to either cut or be cut by a strong magnetic field.

■ geometry

the shape of the resonator plate used in a crystal unit. There are three (3) geometrical forms available Flat, Contoured, and Beveled.

■ geophysics

branch of earth science using physics to study the Earth's surface, interior and atmosphere. Studies also include winds, weather, tides, earthquakes, volcanoes and their effects.

■ geothermal power

geothermal energy is the natural heat of the earth that is conducted or convected to the earth's surface through volcanoes and hot springs. By harnessing this energy and using it to power steam turbines, we can convert geothermal energy into electricity that we can use.

■ gfci (ground fault circuit interrupt)

a type of device, e.g. circuit breaker or receptacle, which detects an abnormal current flow to ground and opens the circuit preventing a hazardous situation.

■ gfi

ground Fault Interrupter -Senses when an appliance on an electrical circuit becomes grounded. The GFI initiates the opening of a circuit breaker to de-energize the circuit.

■ gigabits per second (gbps)

1,000,000,000 bits per second. A measure of transmission speed.

■ gigawatt (gw)

one billion watts; useful for describing the capacity of large electrical energy systems.

■ gilbert

a unit of magnetomotive force in the CGS system.

■ gis

Geographic information system. Where data is assembled, stored, displayed and identified according to its location.

■ GPH

Volumetric flow rate in Gallons Per Hour.

■ GPIB

General Purpose Interface Bus. Also known as IEEE-488 bus. The GPIB standard was designed to connect several instruments to computers for data acquisition and control. Data can be transferred over GPIB at 200 000 bytes per second, over distances of 2 metres.

■ GPM

volumetric flow rate in Gallons Per Minute.

■ GPRS

General Packet Radio Service

■ graded cores

mPP and HF cores are graded

into increments of permeability within their normal ±8% tolerance. It is expressed as a percent deviation from the nominal value.

■ **grain oriented**

silicon steel or other granular magnetic material that has a preferred direction of magnetisation.

■ **gray code**

unit-distance code system in which only one code signal changes with the transition from one measuring step to the next.

■ **green power**

another name for 'renewable energy'.

■ **grid**

the transmission network (or "highway") over which electricity moves from suppliers to consumers.

■ **ground**

1. the electrical neutral line having the same potential as the surrounding earth. 2. The negative side of DC power supply. 3. Reference point for an electrical system.

■ **ground fault circuit interrupter**

a device intended for the protection of personal that functions to de-energize a circuit or portion thereof within an established period of time when a current to ground exceeds some predetermined value that is less than required to operate the overcurrent protection device of the supply circuit.

■ **ground fault protection of equipment**

a system intended to provide protection of equipment from damaging line to ground fault currents by operating to cause a disconnecting means to open all ungrounded conductors of the faulted circuit. This protection is provided at current levels less than those required to protect conductors from damage through the operations of a supply circuit overcurrent device.

■ **ground loop**

condition caused when two or more system components share a common electrical ground line. A feedback loop is unintentionally induced, causing unwanted voltage levels.

■ **ground wire (drain wire)**

An extra conductor (usually a bare wire) added to a cable for connection of the grounding path.

■ **grounded conductor**

a system or circuit conductor that is intentionally grounded, usually gray or white in colour.

■ **grounded junction**

a form of construction of a thermocouple probe where the hot or measuring junction is in electrical contact with the sheath material so that the sheath and thermocouple will have the same electrical potential.

■ **grounded motor**

a motor with an electrical connection between the motor frame and ground.

■ **grounded, effectively**

intentionally connected to earth through a ground connection or connections of sufficiently low impedance and having sufficient current-carrying capacity to prevent the buildup of voltages that may result in undue hazards to connect equipment or to persons.

■ **grounding**

by connecting an electrical circuit to the ground current has a place to safely escape; the third wire on most electrical plugs is the ground wire.

■ **grounding conductor**

a conductor used to connect metal equipment enclosures and/or the system grounded conductor to a grounding electrode, such as the ground wire run to the water pipe at a service; also may be a bare or insulated conductor used to ground motor frames, panel boxes, and other metal equipment enclosures used throughout electrical systems. In most conduit systems, the conduit is used as the ground conductor.

■ **grounding electrode**

the conductor used to connect the grounding electrode to the equipment grounding conductor, to the grounded conductor, or to both, of the circuit at the service equipment or at the source of a separately derived system.

■ **grounding equipment conductor**

the conductor used to connect the noncurrent-carrying metal parts of equipment, raceways, and other enclosures to the system grounded conductor, the grounding electrode conductor, or both, of the circuit at the service equipment or at the source of a separately derived system.

■ **group delay**

the time taken for a narrow band signal to pass from the input to the output of a device.

■ **group delay distortion**

the difference between maximum and minimum group delay in the passband.

■ **gsm**

Global System for Mobile Communications

■ **guarded motor**

an open motor in which all openings giving direct access to live or rotating parts (except smooth shafts) are limited in size by the design of the structural parts or by screens, grills, expanded metal, etc., to prevent accidental contact with such parts. Such openings shall not permit the passage of a cylindrical rod 1/2 inch in diameter.

■ **habitat**

in ecology, the localized environment in which an organism lives. Habitats are often described by the dominant plant type or physical feature, such as a grassland habitat or rocky seashore habitat.

■ **half bridge**

a dual, forward converter, using two power switches can also be called a half bridge. Power, which does not exceed the supply voltage, is delivered to the load only during half the input cycle. This design permits the use of a smaller transformer.

■ **half bridge converter**

converter topology that typically operates as a forward converter but uses a bridge circuit, consisting of two switching transistors, to drive the transformer. Also see bridge converter.

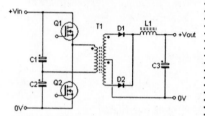

■ **half-duplex**

one way at a time data communication; both devices can transmit and receive data, but only one at a time.

■ **half-wave rectifier**

see **rectification**.

■ **Hall effect transducer**

a device that produces a voltage output dependent upon an applied DC voltage and an incident magnetic field. The magnitude of the output is a function of the field strength and the angle of incidence with the Hall device.

■ **handshake**

An interface procedure that is based on status/data signals that assure orderly data transfer as opposed to asynchronous ex-

change.

■ **hard magnetic material**

a permanent magnet material that has an intrinsic coercivity generally greater than or equal to about 300 Oersteds.

■ **hardcopy**

output in a permanent form (usually a printout) rather than in temporary form, as on disk or display terminal.

■ **hardware**

the electrical, mechanical and electromechanical equipment and parts associated with a computing system, as opposed to its firmware or software.

■ **HART**

Highway Addressable Remote Terminal. Provides digital communication to microprocessor-based (smart) analogue process control instruments.

■ **haversine**

a waveform that is sinusoidal in nature, but consists of a portion of a sine wave superimposed on another waveform. The input current waveform to a typical off-line power supply has the form of a haversine.

■ **hdsl**

high-bit-rate Digital Subscriber Line-Designed to be a cost-effective method of delivering T1/E1 line speeds over unconditioned copper cable, without the use of repeaters.

■ **head loss**

the loss of pressure in a flow system measured using a length parameter (i.e., inches of water, inches of mercury).

■ **head pressure**

pressure in terms of the height of fluid, $P = yrg$, where r = fluid density and y = the fluid column heights. Expression of a pressure in terms of the height of fluid, $r = yrg$, where r is fluid density and y = the fluid column height. g = the acceleration of gravity.

■ **headend**

the source end of a coaxial cable TV system. Often, the site for signal processing equipment essential to proper functioning of a cable system.

■ **headroom**

used in conjunction with series pass regulators, and is the difference between the input and output voltages.

■ **heat**

form of internal energy possessed by a substance by virtue of the kinetic energy in the motion of its molecules or atoms. Heat energy is transferred by conduction, convection and radiation. It always flows from a region of higher temperature (heat intensity) to one of lower temperature. Its effect on a substance may be simply to raise its temperature, or to cause it to expand, melt (if a solid), vaporize (if a liquid), or increase its pressure (if a confined gas).

■ **heat exchanger**

a device which will transfer the heat from inside the motor to an-

other medium, through a radiator type heat exchanger.

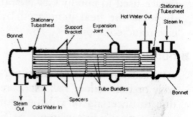

■ **heat flux**

flow rate of heat across or through a material, typically given in $W/cm2$

■ **heat sink**

1. thermodynamic. A body which can absorb thermal energy. 2. Practical. A finned piece of metal used to dissipate the heat of solid state components mounted on it.

■ **heat transfer**

the process of thermal energy flowing from a body of high energy to a body of low energy. Means of transfer are: conduction; the two bodies contact. Convection; a form of conduction where the two bodies in contact are of different phases, i.e. solid and gas. Radiation: all bodies emit infrared radiation.

■ **heat treating**

a process for treating metals where heating to a specific temperature and cooling at a specific rate changes the properties of the metal.

■ **heater**

In an indirectly heated electron tube, the element that supplies heat to the cathode.

■ **heatsink**

device used to conduct away and disperse the heat generated by electronic components.

■ **hedge**

a transaction that is made to partially or fully reduce risk exposure due to uncertain or volatile spot market prices. For example, SCE would enter into a bilateral contract to buy energy at a set price when it expects the price of energy to be much greater in the spot market.

■ **henry**

the basic unit of inductance, identified by the letter "H." One henry of inductance is produced in a closed circuit by a current changing uniformly at the rate of one Ampere per second.

■ **hertz**

the basic unit of measurement of frequency, "Hertz" replaces the term "cycle per second". Used to denote one complete occurrence of an event in one second.

■ **hexadecimal**

refers to a base sixteen number system using the characters 0 through 9 and A through F to represent the values. Machine language programs are often written in hexadecimal notation.

■ **hexagram meter**

remote meter which is read through a scandisc which is located remotely from the meter.

■ **HFC**

Hybrid Fiber-Coaxial

■ **hiccup mode**

operating mode triggered by an output fault condition (short-circuit) in which the converter cycles on and off the duty cycle of on time to off time maintains the internal power dissipation at a safe level until the fault condition is corrected.

■ **high line**

maximum value of input line voltage specified for normal converter operation. Also see **low line and input voltage range.**

■ **high pass filter (hpf)**

a system which allows high frequency signals to pass through while low frequency signals are comparatively attenuated. An differentiator is an example of a LPF. Practically, the current through a capacitor is obtained by differentiating the voltage across it. The voltage across an inductor is obtained by differentiating the current through the inductor.

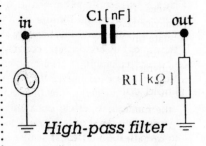

High-pass filter

■ **high potential test (hi-pot test)**

test used to determine whether a converter passes its minimum breakdown voltage specification. Also see **breakdown voltage.**

■ high q filters

a filter circuit that exhibits a high Q factor. It is very frequency sensitive and filters out or allows to pass, only those frequencies within a narrow band.

■ HIPOT

Abbreviation for High Potential, and generally refers to the high voltages used to test dielectric withstand capability for regulatory agency electrical safety requirements.

■ hold

meter HOLD is an external input which is used to stop the A/D process and freeze the display. BCD HOLD is an external input used to freeze the BCD output while allowing the A/D process to continue operation.

■ hold current

the largest steady state current that, under specified ambient conditions, can be passed through a polyswitch device without causing the device to trip. For SiBar devices, the current at which the device resets to a high-impedance state once the surge current dissipates. See also **hold current**. Synonyms: IH,IHOLD

■ hold current minimum

the minimum current required to maintain the device in the on-state. For SiBar thyristors, the current at which the device resets to a high-impedance state once the surge current dissipates.

■ holder

the complete housing for a quartz resonator plate. The holder includes the base and cover.

■ hold-up time

The length of time a power supply can operate in regulation after failure of the AC input. Linears have very short hold-up times due to the CV squared energy storage product of their low voltage secondary side output capacitors. Switchers have longer times due to their higher voltage primary side energy storage capacitors.

■ hole

In a crystal lattice, a point which has been vacated by an electron.

■ Hooke's law

defines the basis for the measurement of mechanical stresses via the strain measurement. The gradient of Hooke's line is defined by the ratio of which is equivalent to the Modulus of Elasticity E (Young's Modulus).

■ horizontal wiring

the span of cabling and connectors between the wiring closet and each drop. It is called horizontal because this type of wiring does not go up or down any floors of a building.

■ horsepower

the measure of rate of work. One horsepower is equivalent to lifting 33,000 pounds to a height of one foot in one minute. The horsepower of a motor is expressed as a function of torque and rpm. For motors the following approximate formula may be used:

$$HP = (T \times RPM) / 5250$$

where HP = horsepower, T = torque (in. lb.ft.), and RPM = revolutions per minute.

■ **host**

the root of the USB architecture which provides signal/data and power (for bus-powered peripherals). In a USB application, the Host is typically within the main CPU.

■ **host utility**

the local franchised utility that serves retail consumers in its service territory

■ **hostile crosstalk**

see crosstalk.

■ **hostile input**

an unselected input carrying a signal which causes unwanted interference and coupling in a desired output. See **crosstalk**.

■ **hot conductor**

a term used to refer to a conductor or wire which is energized.

■ **hot plug-in**

a common requirement in distributed power systems wherein the power board must be capable of being connected/disconnected from the power bus without damage. Power board components must be protected against the resultant high inrush currents.

■ **hot-plug**

the act of making a connection to the output port of a functioning peripheral or host. USB architecture is designed to recognise the connected function and enableO

it by providing necessary power and loading all necessary drivers.

■ **hub**

class of USB equipment that attaches to the Host and provides additional USB output connections for other hubs or functions. May be classified as self-powered hubs or bus-and self-powered hubs.

■ **human machine interface**

also known as man machine interface. The communication between the computer system and the people who use it.

■ **humidity aging test**

a test described in Raychems PS300 publication in which the resistance of a polyswitch device at room temperature is measured before and after aging at an elevated temperature (e.g., 40¡C) and high humidity (e.g., 95% RH) for an extended time (e.g., 1000 hours).

■ **Hurwitz polynomial**

a polynomial with its roots in the open left half plane.

■ **hydrocarbons**

an extensive group of chemicals that always include the elements hydrogen and carbon. Natural sources of hydrocarbons are the by-products of digestion and decomposition (e.g., rotting, spoiling, putrefying). Coal, natural gas, oil, sugar, starches, and plastics are all composed of hydrocarbons. The incomplete combustion of hydrocarbons from fossil fuels contributes to our pollution and global warming problems.

hydroelectric plant

a generating facility that uses falling water as the source of fuel to produce electricity. See **renewable energy**.

hydroelectric power (hep)

electricity generated by moving water. In a typical HEP scheme, water stored in a reservoir, often created by damming a river, is piped into water turbines, coupled to electricity generators. In pumped storage plants, water flowing through the turbines is recycled.

hydrogen ion activity (ah+)

activity of the hydrogen ion in solution. Related to hydrogen ion concentration (CH+) by the activity coefficient for hydrogen (f H+).

hydropower

hydropower is the use of the potential energy contained in water behind dams. Release of water through dam spillways converts potential energy into kinetic energy, which is used to turn a turbine and create power that we can use.

hysteresis

the difference in output when the measurand value is first approached with increasing and then with decreasing values. Expressed in percent of full scale during any one calibration cycle. See also Deadband.

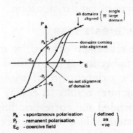

Ferroelectric hysteresis diagram

P_s - spontaneous polarisation
P_r - remanent polarisation
E_c - coercive field

hysteresis (electrode memory)

when an electrode system is returned to a solution, equilibrium is usually not immediate. This phenomenon is often observed in electrodes that have been exposed to the other influences such as temperature, light, or polarisation.

hysteresis

hysteresis means to lag behind. This is the tendency of a magnetic material to retain its magnetisation. Hysteresis causes the graph of magnetic flux density versus magnetising force (B-H curve) to form a loop rather than a line. The area of the loop represents the difference between energy stored and energy released per unit of volume of material per cycle. This difference is called the hysteresis loss.

hysteresis loop

a closed curve obtained for a material by plotting corresponding values of flux density for the ordinate and magnetising force for the abscissa when the material is passing through a complete cycle between definite limits of either magnetising force or flux density. If the material is not driven into saturation it is said to be on a minor loop.

■ **hysteresis loss**

the resistance offered by materials to becoming magnetised (magnetic orientation of molecular structure) results in energy being expended and corresponding loss. Hysteresis loss in a magnetic circuit is the energy expended to magnetise and demagnetise the core.

■ **HZ**

the abbreviation of the word 'Hertz.'

■ **i**

symbol for electric current.

■ **i/o**

input/output. A data acquisition system monitors signals through its inputs, and sends control signals through its outputs.

■ **I2r**

losses due to current flowing in a conductor caused by resistance (equals the current squared times the resistance.)

■ **IAD**

Integrated Access Devices

■ **IC**

Integrated Circuit (electronic components fabricated on a semiconductor substrate which cannot be divided without losing its function).

■ **icon**

a graphic functional symbol display. A graphic representation of

a function or functions to be performed by the computer.

■ **ICP**

Integrated Circuit Piezoelectric; term sometimes used to describe an accelerometer with built-in electronics.

■ **ID**

abbreviation for Inside Diameter.

■ **identification**

in most instances, the following information will help identify a motor:
1. Frame designation (actual frame size in which the motor is built).
2. Horsepower, speed, design and enclosure.
3. Voltage, frequency and number of phases of power supply.
4. Class of insulation and time rating.
5. Application

■ **ISDL**

ISDN Digital Subscriber Line

■ **IEEE**

Institute of Electrical and Electronics Engineers. An American Society that, amongst other things, establishes international standards in the computing, electronic and telecommunications fields.

■ **ieee-488 bus**

see **GPIB**.

■ **ih**

the largest steady state current that, under specified ambient conditions, can be passed through a polyswitch device without causing the device to trip. For SiBar devices, the current at which the device resets to a high-impedance state once the surge current dissipates. See also **hold current**. Synonyms: IHOLD

■ **ihold**

the largest steady state current that, under specified ambient conditions, can be passed through a polyswitch device without causing the device to trip. For SiBar devices, the current at which the device resets to a high-impedance state once the surge current dissipates. See also **hold current**. Synonyms: IH

■ **ILEC**

Incumbent Local Exchange Carriers (formerly RBOC)

■ **imaginary crossovers**

consider a negative feedback system with open loop transfer function kL(s) = k n(s)/d(s) where k is a scalar parameter. The term imaginary crossovers, or imaginary crossover frequencies, refers to pairs (k, s) on the root locus (k >= 0) or complementary root locus (k <= 0) where s = jw lies on the imaginary axis; i.e. imaginary crossovers refer to pairs (k, s) where s is an imaginary closed loop pole. Suppose that k is non-zero. In such a case, the corresponding imaginary crossovers are called phase crossovers or phase crossover frequencies. The imaginary crossovers, or phase crossover frequencies, for k > 0 (i.e. on the root locus) correspond to w values such that the angle of the open loop transfer function L(jw) is -

180 degrees +/- any integer multiple of 360 degrees. The imaginary crossovers, or phase crossover frequencies, for k < 0 (i.e. on the complementary root locus) correspond to w values such that the angle of the open loop transfer function L(jw) is 0 degrees +/- any integer multiple of 360 degrees.

■ **imax**

the highest fault current that can safely be used to trip a polyswitch device under specified conditions. Typically the lower the voltage dropped across the polyswitch device in its tripped state, the higher the maximum interrupt current. Maximum interrupt currents are usually shown in this Databook at the maximum voltage. It may be possible to use a polyswitch device at a higher interrupt current, but each such use must be individually qualified.

■ **IML**

Interface Management Language. A programming language used to communicate with measurement instruments.

■ **impedance**

the impedance of an inductor is the total resistance to the flow of current, including the AC and DC component. The DC component of the impedance is simply the DC resistance of the winding. The AC component of the impedance includes the inductor reactance. The following formula calculates the inductive reactance of an ideal inductor (i.e. one with no losses) to a sinusoidal AC signal. (Z

■ impulse response

the impulse response of a system is the response of the system to a Dirac-delta function (distribution). Unless otherwise specified, a unit delta function input under zero initial conditions is implied.

■ in sight from

(within sight from, within sight) Where this *Code* specifies that one equipment shall be 'in sight from', 'within sight from' or 'm within sight', etc. of another equipment, the specified equipment is to be visible and not more that 50′ distant from the other

■ incremental current

the DC bias current flowing through an inductor which causes an inductance drop of 5% from the initial zero DC bias inductance value. This current level indicates where the inductance can be expected to drop significantly if the DC bias current is increased further. This applies mostly to ferrite cores in lieu of iron powder. These core materials exhibit soft saturation characteristics, which means their inductance drop from higher DC levels is much more gradual than ferrite cores. The rate at which the inductance will drop is also a function of the core shape.

■ incremental measuring system

measuring method by which the measuring value is derived by the summation (counting) of increments (measuring steps).

■ incremental permeability (μinc)

the permeability of a magnetic material about a specified operating point and applied magnetic field strength, especially under DC bias conditions. The incremental permeability is expressed as the slope of the B-H characteristic about the given operating point (dB/dH).

■ independent system operator

a new entity that will manage the power grid for California to ensure continued system reliability.

■ individual port protection

protection method where each output is protected by one circuit protection device (or output). For devices with multiple outputs per device, isolation is provided so that a port can respond to a fault condition without impacting the performance of the other port(s).

■ induced noise

noise generated in a circuit by a varying magnetic field produced by another circuit.

■ inductance

that property of a circuit element which tends to oppose any change in the current flowing through it. The inductance for a given inductor is influenced by the core material, core shape and size, the turns count of the coil, and the shape of the coil. Inductors most often have their inductance values expressed in microHenries (μH) or milliHenries (mH).

■ inductance factor (al)

the inductance rating of a core in nanoHenries per turn squared (nH/N2) based on a peak flux density of 10 gauss (1 milliTesla) at a frequency of 10 kHz. An AL value of 40 would produce 400µH of inductance for 100 turns and 40mH for 1000 turns.

■ induction motor

an induction motor is an alternating current motor in which the primary winding on one member (usually the stator) is connected to the power source and a secondary winding or a squirrel-cage secondary winding on the other member (usually the rotor) carries the induced current. There is no physical electrical connection to the secondary winding, its current is induced.

■ inductor

a passive component designed to resist changes in current. Inductors are often referred to as AC resistors. The ability to resist changes in current and the ability to store energy in its magnetic field account for the bulk of the useful properties of inductors. Current passing through an inductor will produce a magnetic field, which induces a voltage, which opposes the field-producing current. This property of impeding changes in current is known as inductance.

■ industry restructuring

changing the electric market structure by opening the generation of electricity and electric retail services to competition.

■ inertial load

a load (flywheel, fan, etc.) which tends to cause the motor shaft to continue to rotate after the power has been removed (stored kinetic energy). If this continued rotation cannot be tolerated, some mechanical or electrical braking means must normally be applied . This application may require a special motor due to the energy required to accelerate the inertia. Inertia is measured in either lb.ft.^{2} or OZ.jn.^{2}

Inertia reflected to the shaft of the motor = (Load RPM) ^{2}/Motor RPM

■ infrared

an area in the electromagnetic spectrum extending beyond red light from 760 nanometers to 1000 microns (106 nm). It is the form of radiation used for making non-contact temperature measurements.

■ inhibit

the ability to electrically turn off the output of a power supply from a remote location.

■ initial permeability (µi)

the value of permeability at a peak AC flux density of 10 Gauss (1 milliTesla).

■ initial permeability (no)

permeability=u=B/H Initial permeability is that value of permeability when Bac=10gs.

■ initial resistance

the resistance of a polyswitch device under specified conditions (e.g., 20 °C), before connection into a circuit. Devices of a particular type will be delivered with a range of resistances; therefore, a minimum value, Rmin, and/or a maximum value, Rmax, are often given. Synonyms: Resistance, Base Resistance, Rmin, or Rmax

■ initial unbalance

initial unbalance is that unbalance of any kind that exists in the rotor before balancing.

■ injection molding

the process used to inject molten polymer into a mold. Connector backshells are often injection molded.

■ input

data entering a device from the environment. A signal being monitored by a data acquisition system.

■ input bus

a circuit path on the input side of a switching array which connects to the inputs of one or more crosspoint switches. Each input connector leads to an input bus.

■ input current

current drawn from the input power bus by a converter when operating under nominal conditions

■ input impedance

the resistance of a panel meter as seen from the source. In the case of a voltmeter, this resistance has to be taken into account when the source impedance is high; in the case of an ammeter, when the source impedance is low.

■ input line filter

a power filter placed on the input to a circuit or assembly that attenuates noise introduced from the power bus. The filter is designed to reject lise within a frequency band. Typically these filters arc low-pass filters meaning they pass low frequency signals such as the DC power and attenuate higher frequency signal which consist of mainly noise. Band pass or low pass filters are commonly made up of inductor and capacitor combinations. (Also see Noise, Attenuation, EMI and Pi-Filter).

■ input reflected ripple current

AC component (typically generated by the switching circuit) measured at the input of a converter. Given as a peak-to-peak or RMS value.

■ input resistance (impedance)

the input resistance of a pH meter is the resistance between the glass electrode terminal and the reference electrode terminal. The potential of a pH-measuring electrode chain is always subject to a voltage division between the total electrode resistance and the input resistance.

■ input surge current

see **inrush current**.

■ input transient

spike or step change in the input to a converter. Input transient protection circuits arc used to shield sensitive components (such as the semiconductor switch) from possible damage due to transients.

■ **input voltage range**

minimum and maximum input voltage limits within which a converter operates to specifications. Often given as a ratio of high line to low line (i.e. a range of 9VDC to 18VDC is 2:1)

■ **inrush current**

the peak current flowing into a power supply the instant AC power is applied. This peak is usually much higher than the steady state input current due to the charging of the input filter capacitors.

■ **inrush current limiting**

protection circuit that limits the current a converter draws at turn on.

■ **insertion loss**

the loss in load power due to the insertion of a component or device at some point in a transmission system. (Generally expressed as the ratio in decibels of power received at the load before insertion of the apparatus, to the power received at the load after insertion.)

■ **instantaneous value**

the value of an alternating current or voltage at any specified instant in a cycle.

■ **institute of electrical and electronic engineers (ieee)**

professional Organisation that defines network standards. IEEE LAN standards are the predominant LAN

standards today, including protocols similar or virtually equivalent to Ethernet and Token Ring.

■ **instrument**

any item of electrical or electronic equipment which is designed to carry out a specific function or set of functions. For example an electronic balance, a gas analyser or a chromatograph.

■ **insulated gate bipolar transistor (igbt)**

power semiconductor device available for use in power conversion circuits.

■ **insulated junction**

See **ungrounded junction**

■ **insulation**

properly insulated transformers can withstand severe environmental conditions and remain in service for many years. The temperature of operation and the dielectric withstanding voltage (hipot) will determine the type and amount of insulation needed.

■ **insulation displacement contact**

A means of terminating wires without the need of stripping down to the bare wire.

■ **insulation resistance**

the ohmic resistance of insulation. It degrades quickly as humidity increases. Lower insulation resistance provides a path for leakage current to ground. This is very critical when making measurements on semiconductor components where picoamp measurements are being made.

■ insulation systems

five specialized elements are used, which together constitute the motor's insulation system. The following are typical in an AC motor:

1. *Turn-To-Turn Insulation* between separate wires in each coil. (Usually enamel on random wound coils of smaller motors - tape on 'form wound' coils of larger motors.)

2. *Phase-To-Phase Insulation* between adjacent coils in different phase groups. (A separate sheet material on smaller motors - not required on form wound coils because the tape also performs this function.)

3. *Phase-To-Ground Insulation* between windings as a whole and the 'ground' or metal part of the motor. (A sheet material, such as the liner used in stator slots, provides both di-electric and mechanical protection.)

4. *Slot Wedge* to hold conductors firmly in the slot.

5. *Impregnation* to bind all the other components together and fill in the air spaces. (A total impregnation, applied in a fluid form and hardened, provides protection against contaminants.

■ insulator

a material which tends to resist the flow of electric current (paper, glass, etc.) In a motor the insulation serves two basic functions:

1. separates the various electrical components from one another.

2. it protects itself and the electrical components from attack of contaminants and other destructive forces.

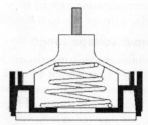

■ integer

a positive or negative whole number, or 0.

■ integral

a form of temperature control.

■ integral coupling

innovative angle encoder design with built-in coupling, located preferably on the stator-side.

■ integrated circuit

electronic components fabricated on a semiconductor substrate. An integrated circuit cannot be divided without losing its function.

■ integration time

the time over which an integrating A-D converter averages the input signal. If chosen appropriately will average over a complete mains cycle thereby helping to reduce mains frequency interference.

■ interchangeability error

a measurement error that can occur if two or more probes are used to make the same measurement. It is caused by a slight variation in characteristics of different probes.

■ interface

a shared boundary. It might be a

piece of hardware used between two pieces of equipment, or a software display communicating between the computer system and the people who use it.

■ **interface**

1) the point at which two systems or pieces of equipment are connected. 2) a connection between two systems or devices. A shared boundary defined by common physical interconnection characteristics, signal characteristics, and meanings of interchanged signals.

■ **interferential measuring system**

photoelectric measuring system with a phase grating scale where scanning signals are produced via the interference of diffracted beams.

■ **intermittent duty**

a requirement of service that demands operation for alternate intervals of (1) load and no load; or (2) load and rest; or (3) load, no load and rest; such alternate intervals being definitely specified.

■ **internal model principle**

refers to the idea that to follow a reference command r or reject a disturbance d, one needs a model of that reference command or disturbance within the feedback loop.

■ **internal power dissipation**

power dissipated (as heat) within the converter during normal operation. Primarily a function of the power handling capability and efficiency of the converter. Inter-

nal power dissipation is normally given as a maximum specification that cannot be exceeded without risking damage to the converter.

■ **internal reference electrode (element)**

the reference electrode placed internally in a glass electrode.

■ **international electrotechnical commission**

organisation based in Switzerland that sets standards for electronic products and components: IEC does not conduct any testing; however, their standards have been adopted by many of the national safety/standards agencies.

■ **interpolation**

method for producing measuring increments which are smaller than a fourth of the scanning signal period.

■ **interpoles**

an auxiliary set of field poles carrying armature current to reduce the field flux caused by armature reaction in a DC motor.

■ **interpreter**

a system program that converts and executes each instruction of a high-level language program into machine code as it runs, before going onto the next instruction.

■ **interrupt**

to stop a process in such a way that it can be resumed.

■ **interrupter rating**

the highest current at rated voltage that a device is intended to interrupt under standard test conditions.

■ **intranet**

a private network that uses internet software and standards.

■ **intrinsic**

a word used to indicate a semiconductor that has no impurities.

■ **intrinsically safe**

an instrument which will not produce any spark or thermal effects under normal or abnormal conditions that will ignite a specified gas mixture.

■ **inverter**

an electronic device that converts fixed frequency and fixed voltages to variable frequency and voltage. Enables the user to electrically vary the speed of an AC motor.

■ **inverter transformer**

a transformer driven in such a manner that an applied DC power is converted to AC power (square waveform). Quite often the core is driven into saturation to accomplish this function.

■ **ionic mobility**

defined similarly to the mobility of nonelectrolytic particles, viz., as the speed that the ion obtains in a given solvent when influenced by unit power.

■ **ionic strength**

the weight concentration of ions in solution, computed by multiplying the concentration of each ion in solution (C) by the correspond-ing square of the charge on the ion (Z) summing this product for all ions in solution and dividing by 2:ionic strength - $1/2 \_ Z2 C$.

■ **IP**

Internet Protocol

■ **IPTS-48**

International Practical Temperature Scale of 1948. Fixed points in thermometry as specified by the Ninth General Conference of Weights and Measures which was held in 1948.

■ **IPTS-68**

International Practical Temperature Scale of 1968. Fixed points in thermometry set by the 1968 General Conference of Weights and Measures.

■ **iron-core coil/transformer**

coil/transformer wound around an iron core to increase its inductance. At audio frequencies the iron core consists of laminations of silicon steel insulated from each other by varnish or shellac. At radio frequencies the core consists of powdered iron mixed in a binder which insulates the particles from each other.

■ **ISA**

Industry Standard Architecture. An ISA expansion slot lets you plug data acquisition boards into PCs.

■ **isc max**

the maximum short circuit a polyswitch device is tested at the maximum operating voltage as specified.

ISDN

Integrated Services Digital Network- A CCITT networking standard devised to provide end-to-end, simultaneous handling of digitized voice and data traffic on the same link

ISO

International Organisation for Standardisation, which is made up of national members. A member is the 'most representative of standardisation in its country'. For example BSI (British Standards Institute), DIN (Deutsches Institut für Normung) and ANSI (American National Standards Institute).

ISO 9001

a series of quality standards established by the International Organisation of Standardisation, that outline the requirements for quality management systems.

isolated output

see **floating output**

isolation

electrical separation between the input and output of a converter; normally determined by transformer characteristics and component spacing. Referring to isolation is specified in values of resistance (RISO, typically megohms) and capacitance (CISO, typically pF).

isolation between inputs

a transient at an input can also propagate to other equipment connected to that input. This is prevented by providing isolation between inputs.

isolation capacitance

see **isolation**.

isolation resistance

see **isolation**.

isolation to earth or system

a high transient voltage at one input may damage not only the input circuit, but the rest of the data acquisition hardware, and, by propagating through the signal conditioning and A-D circuits, eventually damage the computer system as well. You can prevent this type of damage by isolating the input from the earth of the data acquisition and computer hardware.

isolation transformer

transformer with a one-to-one turns ratio, connected between the a.c. power input to a piece of equipment and the a.c. line to minimise shock hazard.

isolation voltage

maximum voltage (AC or DC) that can be continuously applied between isolated circuits without a breakdown occurring. On converters, this is normally specified as input-output or input-case isolation. Minimum isolation voltage levels be maintained to meet most safety regulations. Also see **Breakdown Voltage, High Potential and Isolation.**

isopotential point

a potential which is not affected by temperature changes. It is the pH value at which dE/dt for a given electrode pair is zero. Normally, for a glass electrode and SCE reference, this potential is obtained approximately when immersed in pH 7 buffer.

■ **isothermal**

A process or area that is a constant temperature.

■ **isotropic**

having magnetic properties that are independent of the magnet orientation. Most magnetic materials are anisotropic as cast or powdered: each crystallite has a preferred direction of magnetic orientation. If the particles are not physically oriented during manufacture of the magnet, this results in random arrangement of the particles and magnetic domains, and produces isotropic magnetic properties. Conversely, orienting the material during the manufacture results in an anisotropic magnet.

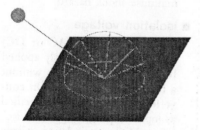

■ **isp**

internet Service Provider

■ **it**

the smallest steady state current that, if passed through a polyswitch device, will cause the device to trip, under specified conditions.

■ **itu**

international Telecommunications Union

■ **ixc**

interexchange Carrier- (1)A long-distance telephone company offering circuit-switched, leased-line or packet-switched service or some combination. (2) Any individual, partnership, association, joint-stock company, trust, governmental entity or corporation engaged for hire in interstate or foreign communication by wire or radio, between two or more exchanges.

■ **j seconds (dc motors)**

j is the per unit moment of inertia. It is defined as the time in seconds to accelerate the motor armature to rated base speed using rated full load torque.

■ **jack**

The female receptacle - usually found on equipment.

■ **jackscrew**

a device used for leveling the positioning of a motor. These devices are adjustable screws fitting on the base or motor frame.
Also a device for removing endshields from a motor assembly.

■ **jordan form of a matrix**

while some n x n matrices are not diagonalisable (i.e. do not have a set of independent eigenvectors), all matrices can be placed in Jordan Form.

■ **joule**

(symbol J) named in honor of

British physicist James P. Joule (rhymes with pool) who proved in 1843 that a specific amount of work was converted into a specific amount of heat. A joule is now a unit for all forms of energy. One joule of work is done when the force of one NEWTON is exerted on an object moving in the direction of the force, a distance of one meter. It takes about one joule to lift an apple over your head. As the transition from the English system of energy measurement to the international system of units (SI) picks up momentum, we will soon become accustomed to hearing more frequently of kilojoules (Kj) and megajoules (Mj). One kilowatt-hour = 3.6 x 10^6 joules. One calorie = 4.187 joules.

■ journal

a journal is that part of a rotor that is in contact with or supported by a bearing in which it revolves.

■ j-type thermocouple

iron-constantan thermocouple with a temperature range of 0 to 750 °C.

■ jumper

Single twisted pairs used for cross connecting between 66, 110, or Krone blocks.

■ junction

the point in a thermocouple where the two dissimilar metals are joined.

■ junction diode

a diode consisting of a PN junction and suitable connecting leads.

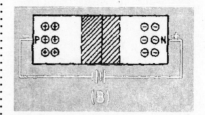

■ k

a symbol for a thousand, from kilo.

■ k

a unit of stored data. 1k = 2^{10} = 1024.
Also stands for a degree on the Kelvin temperature scale.

■ Kalman filter

a model based filter which is used to estimate the state of a system from knowledge of noisy output and input measurements. A least squares error criterion is used to construct optimal linear estimates based on first and second order statistics for each noise source (e.g. sensor noise and process noise). Developed by R.E. Kalman during the early 1960's. Also see **state estimator and observer**.

■ kelvin

Symbol K. The unit of absolute or thermodynamic temperature scale based upon the Celsius scale with 100 units between the ice point and boiling point of water. 0°C = 273.15K (there is no degree (°) symbol used with the Kelvin scale).

■ kHz

the abbreviation for "kiloHertz," used to describe the frequency of a crystal or oscillator in terms of thousands of Hertz (cycles per second). A frequency specified as "10.0 kHz" would be understood as being a frequency of 10,000 Hertz (cycles per second). A frequency specified as "10,000 kHz" would be understood as being a frequency of 10,000,000 Hertz (cycles per second).

■ **kilo**

a prefix, abbreviated "k," used to denote units of thousands. One "Kilo" is one thousand. In our industry, a frequency of one kilohertz is a frequency of one thousand hertz (cycles per second).

■ **kilobits per second (kbps)**

1,000 bits per second. A measure of transmission speed.

■ **kilowatt**

a measure of electric energy equal to 1,000 watts. Put another way, it's the amount of electric energy required to light ten 100-watt light bulbs.

■ **kilowatt-hour**

a measure of energy use over time. Utility companies typically sell energy as kilowatt-hours (kWh). A kilowatt-hour is 1,000 watts used for one hour. If you purchased a kilowatt-hour from your utility for less than a dime, you could burn ten, 100-watt incandescent light bulbs for one hour. Other electrical appliances such as stoves, heaters and blow dryers, would operate for less time for that same nickel because their energy demands are greater for their operation. (1 kWh = 3.6 x 106J or 36,000,000 J.)

■ **kilowatt-hour (kWh)**

one thousand watts of power used in one hour. A watt-hour is the basic unit for measuring electric energy consumption.

■ **kinetic energy**

energy associated with mass in motion, i.e., $1/2$ rV^2 where r is the density of the moving mass and V is its velocity.

■ **kinetic theory**

theory describing the physical properties of matter in terms of the behavior — principally movement — of its component atoms or molecules. The temperature of a substance is dependent on the velocity of movement of its constituent particles, increased temperature being accompanied by increased movement. As gas consists of rapidly moving atoms or molecules and, according to kinetic theory, it is their continual impact on the walls of the containing vessel that accounts for the pressure of the gas. The slowing of molecular motion as temperature falls, according to kinetic theory, accounts for the physical properties of liquids and solids, culminating in the concept of no molecular motion at absolute zero (0K/-460F).

■ **knee (of the demagnetisation curve)**

in the second and fourth quadrants of the hysteresis loop, some materials such as ferrite and rare earth exhibit a distinct knee, or rapid change in slope of the intrinsic curve. The location of the knee is of interest to designers.

kool mu (r)

kool Mu (r) is a magnetic material that has an inherent distributed air gap. The distributed air gap allowes the core to store higher levels of magnetic~ when compared to other magnetic materials such as ferrites. This characteristic allows a higher DC current level to flow through the inductor before the inductor saturates. Kool Mu (r) material is an alloy that is made up of basically nickel and iron powder (approx. 50% of each) and is available in several permeabilities. It has a higher permeability than powdered iron and also lower core losses. Kool Mu (r) is required to be pressed at much higher pressure than powdered iron material. The manufacturing process includes an annealing step that relieves the pressure put onto the powdered metals which restores their desirable magnetic properties. Thus, the powdered particles require a high temperature insulation as compared to powdered iron. Kool Mu (r) performs well in switching power applications. The relative cost is significantly higher than powdered iron.

k-type connector

a small type of threaded coaxial signal connector typically used in higher frequency applications. This connector is typically usable as high as 40GHz. It may be mated by an SMA connector with much lower performance.

k-type thermocouple

chromel-Alumel thermocouple

with a temperature range of -200 to 1200 °C.

kVa

kilovolt amperes (1000-volt amps).

kW

an abbreviation for Kilowatt.

kWh

an abbreviation for Kilowatt-Hours.

labeled

items to which a label, trademark, or other identifying mark of nationally recognised testing labs has been attached to indentify the items as having been tested and meeting appropriate standards.

lag

1. a time delay between the output of a signal and the response of the instrument to which the signal is sent. 2. A time relationship between two waveforms where a fixed reference point on one wave occurs after the same point of the reference wave.

laminar flow

Streamlined flow of a fluid where viscous forces are more significant than inertial forces, generally below a Reynolds number of 2000.

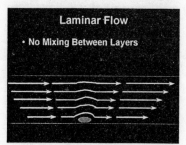

Laminar Flow
• No Mixing Between Layers

■ laminated cores

cores constructed by stacking multiple laminations on top of each other. The laminations are offered in a variety of materials and thickness. Some laminations are made to have the grains oriented to minimise the core losses and give higher permeabilities. Each lamination has an insulated surface that is commonly an oxide finish. Laminated cores are used in some inductor designs, but are more common in a wide variety of transformer applications.

■ laminations

supplied in stamped letter shapes such as EIÓ, ELÓ, EEÓ, FÓ, or UIÓ, they are composed of silicon iron and nickel alloys. Audio and telecommunication transformers use nickel alloys, while silicon iron is generally used for line frequency power transformers.

■ LAN

Local Area Network. A data communication system connecting devices in the same vicinity. Data is transferred without the use of public communications. Examples of LANs are Ethernet, token ring and Modbus.

■ laplace transform

useful for solving problems involving systems described by linear ordinary differential equations with constant coefficients. The Unilateral Laplace Transform of a function f is denoted by the symbol F(s) and is defined as the integral from 0- to infinity of f(t)exp(-st).

The resulting function F is defined for those values s in the complex plane for which the Laplace integral makes sense; i.e. is finite. Such values of s are said to make up the regions of convergence of the function F. See **region of convergence.**

■ large motors

usually refers to AC motors in 5,000 series frames and above and to 500 series frames and larger in DC.

■ large scale integration (lsi)

the combining of about 1,000 to 10,000 circuits on a single chip. Typical examples of LSI circuits are memory chips and microprocessor.

■ last mile

a reference to the local loop, the distance between a local telco office and the subscriber, a distance actually about 0 to 3 miles (0 to 4 kilometers).

■ latching

in relay or switching technology, this refers to the ability to keep the contact status in place even if power is removed from the equipment.

■ latent heat

expressed in BTU per pound. The amount of heat needed (absorbed) to convert a pound of boiling water to a pound of steam.

■ layer winding

a transformer winding technique where the primary and secondary windings are wound over each other and separated by an insulation layer.

■ leakage current

a term relating to current flowing between the AC supply wires and earth ground. The term does not necessarily denote a fault condition. In power supplies, leakage current usually refers to the 60 Hertz current which flows through the EMI filter capacitors which are connected between the AC lines and ground (Y caps).

■ leakage flux

the small fraction of the total magnetic flux in a transformer or common mode choke that does not contribute to the magnetic coupling of the windings. In a transformer with a single set of primary and secondary windings, the leakage flux is that portion of flux that is produced by the primary that does not link the secondary. The presence of leakage flux in a transformer or common mode choke is modeled as a small leakage inductance in series with each winding. It is measured at one winding with all other windings shorted.

■ leakage inductance

a small inductance associated with those flux lines of a transformer winding which are not magnetically coupled to the other windings of the transformer.

■ leakage rate

the maximum rate at which a fluid is permitted or determined to leak through a seal. The type of fluid,

the differential Limits of Error: A tolerance band for the thermal electric response of thermocouple wire expressed in degrees or percentage defined by ANSI specification MC-96.1 (1975).

■ leased line

a transmission line reserved by a communication carrier for the private use of a customer.

■ least-squares line

the straight line for which the sum of the squares of the residuals (deviations) is minimised.

■ LEC

Local Exchange Carrier

■ left hand generator rule

a method of determining the direction of current flow (polarity) in a conductor, as follows: Extend the thumb first finger, and second finger of the left hand at right angles to each other. When the thumb is pointed in the direction (upward or downward) of conductor motion as it passes through the magnetic field, and the first finger is pointed to the south pole of the magnetic field (matching the direction of magnetic flux), the second finger will point in the direction of current flow (toward the negative pole or terminal).

■ IFM

Linear Feet Per Minute, which is a measure of air velocity used to cool a power converter.

■ life cycle

the minimum number of pressure cycles the transducer can endure and still remain within a specified tolerance.

▣ life test

reliability test in which a converter is operated (typically under accelerated conditions) over some period of time in order to approximate its life expectancy.

▣ lifeline pots

a minimal telephone service designed to extend a "lifeline" to the telephone system in case of emergency, particularly when electric power is lost.

▣ LIFO

Last In First Out. Describes a stack method of data storage.

▣ light

electromagnetic waves in the visible range, having a wavelength from about 400 nanometers in the extreme violet to about 770 nanometers in the extreme red. Light is considered to exhibit particle and wave properties, and the fundamental particle, or quantum, of light is called the photon. The speed of light (and of all electromagnetic radiation) in a vacuum is approximately 186,000 mi/ 300,000 km per second, and is a universal constant denoted by c.

▣ limits of error

a tolerance band for the thermal electric response of thermocouple wire expressed in degrees or percentage defined by ANSI specification MC-96.1 (1975).

▣ LIMS

Laboratory Information Manage-ment system.

▣ line

bus used to deliver power to the input terminals of a converter. Also see **Bus, High Line** and **Low Line.**

▣ line code

any method of converting digital information to analog form for transmission on a telephone line. 2B1Q, DMT, and CAP are all line codes.

▣ line effect

see **line regulation.**

▣ line regulation

power supply regulation technique in which the regulating device (typically a transistor) is placed in series or parallel with the load. Voltage variations across the load are controlled by changing the effective resistance of the regulating device to dissipate unused power. Also see **series regulator, shunt regulator** and **post regulation.**

▣ line transient

see **input transient.**

▣ linear material

magnetic material that exhibits fairly constant permeability over a wide range of MMF.

▣ linear power transformer

transformers that generally operate between 47Hz and 400Hz in power conversion, which alter the input voltage needed for the load. Linear power transformers are very inefficient.

■ linear regulation

power supply regulation technique in which the regulating device (typically a transistor) is placed in series or parallel with the load. Voltage variations across the load are controlled by changing the effective resistance of the regulating device to dissipate unused power. Also see **series regulator, shunt regulator and post regulation.**

■ linear regulator

a regulating technique where a dissipative active device such as a transistor is placed in series with a power supply output to regulate the output voltage.

■ linear time invariant (LTI) system

refers to dynamical systems which are linear and time-invariant.

■ linearity

ideally an A-D or D-A converter converts the input or output range into equal steps. In practice the steps are not exactly equal. Linearity, or non-linearity, is a measure of how close the steps approach equality.

■ link

physical connection between two nodes in a network. It can consist of a data communication circuit or a direct channel (cable) connection. Also an LED signal that indicates connection has been established.

■ liquid junction potential

the potential difference existing between a liquid-liquid boundary.

The sign and size of this potential depends on the composition of the liquids and the type of junction used.

■ listed

equipment or materials included in a list published by an Organisation acceptable to the authority having jurisdiction and concerned with product evaluation, that maintains periodic inspection of production of listed equipment or materials, and whose listing states either that the equipment or material meets appropriate designated standards or has been tested and found suitable for use in specified manner.

■ litz wire

wire consisting of a number of separately insulated strands that are woven or bunched together such that each strand tends to take all possible positions in the cross section of the wire as a whole. The current through each individual strand is divided equally since this wire design equalizes the flux linkages and reactance of the individual strands. In other words, a litz conductor has lower AC losses than comparable solid wire conductors which becomes important as the operating frequency increases (Also see **skin effect).**

■ LMDS

Local Multipoint Distribution Service

■ load

the amount of electric power delivered or required at any specified point in a system; load also refers to the amount of electricity required by a customer or a piece of equipment. When the term refers to the sum of the demands in an electric system it is usually expressed in megawatts.

load capacitance

the value of capacitance used in conjunction with the crystal unit. Load capacitance is a parameter specified by the customer, typically expressed in pF (picoFarads).

load decoupling

placement of filter components (typically mF capacitors) at the power terminals of the load in order to reduce noise.

load impedance

the impedance presented to the output terminals of a transducer by the associated external circuitry.

load loss

these losses are caused by the resistance of the windings under loaded conditions.

load profiling

the study of the consumption habits of consumers to estimate the amount of power they use at various times of the day and for which they are billed. Load profiling is an alternative to precise metering.

load regulation

percentage change in output voltage caused by varying the output load over a specified range (with input line, temperature, etc. remaining constant).

load resonance

the condition existing when a crystal unit is operated in conjunction with load capacitance.

local area network (lan)

a network that remains within one facility (department, office, building, campus).

local area transport area (lata)

1) a geographic area established for the provision and administration of communications service. It encompasses one or more designated exchanges, which are grouped to serve common social, economic and other purposes. 2) Contiguous local exchange areas that include every point served by a LEC within an existing community of interest and that serve as the dividing line for the allocation of assets and liabilities between the IXC and the LEC. 3) A telephone company term that defines a geographic area, sometimes corresponds to an area code.

local loop

refers to the physical copper pair or loop of wire from Central Office to the subscriber.

local sensing

using the output terminals of the converter to provide feedback to voltage regulation circuits. Also see **remote sensing.**

location, damp

a location subject to moderate amount of moisture such as some basements, barns, cold storage, warehouse and the like.

location, dry

a location not normally subject to dampness or wetness: a location classified as dry may be temporarily subject to dampness or wetness, as in case of a building under construction.

location, wet

a location subject to saturation with water or other liquids.

lock ring

meter ring with locking device to secure socket meters.

lock ring key

used to open locking device on lock ring.

locked rotor current

steady state current taken from the line with the rotor at standstill (at rated voltage and frequency). This is the current seen when starting the motor and load.

locked rotor torque

the minimum torque that a motor will develop at rest for all angular positions of the rotor (with rated voltage applied at rated frequency).

logarithmic scale

a method of displaying data (in powers of ten) to yield maximum range while keeping resolution at the low end of the scale.

logic enable

the ability to turn a power supply on and off with a TTL signal. A logic low generally turns the sup-

ply off; a logic high turns it on.

logic inhibit/enable

signal (typically TTL/CMOS compatible) used to turn a power supply output on/off. Also called Remote On/Off.

long term stability

change in output voltage of a converter over time with all other factors (line, load, temp. etc.) remaining constant. Expressed as a percent, the output change is primarily due to component aging.

loop resistance

The total resistance of a thermocouple circuit caused by the resistance of the thermocouple wire. Usually used in reference to analog pyrometers which have typical loop resistance requirements of 10 ohms.

looping input

an input which passes a video signal in and out of a device without terminating the cable or affecting the signal quality. Looping inputs use two connectors normally wired together with no active components between them. If the looping feature is not used, a 75 ohm terminator should be placed on the second connector, or a provision for switching in a 75 ohm termination internally.

loss budget (fiber optic)

the maximum amount of power that is allowed to be lost per optical link.

losses

a motor converts electrical energy

into a mechanical energy and in so doing, encounters losses. These losses are all the energy that is put into a motor and not transformed to usable power but are converted into heat causing the temperature of the windings and other motor parts to rise.

■ low line

minimum value of input line voltage specified for normal converter operation.

■ low noise lamp

a specially constructed lamp designed to produce less audible noise in dimming applications.

■ low pass filter (lpf)

a system which allows low frequency signals to pass through while high frequency signals are comparatively attenuated. An integrator is an example of a LPF. Practically, the current through an inductor is obtained by integrating the voltage across it. The voltage across a capacitor is obtained by integrating the current through the inductor.

■ low thermal

see Contact Potential.

■ LSD (Least-Significant Digit)

The rightmost active (non-dummy) digit of the display.

■ ls-ttl compatible

for digital input circuits, a logic 1 is obtained for inputs of 2.0 to 5.5 V which can source 20 μA, and a logic 0 is obtained for inputs of 0 to 0.8 V which can sink 400 μA.

For digital output signals, a logic 1 is represented by 2.4 to 5.5 V with a current source capability of at least 400 μA; and a logic 0 is represented by 0 to 0.6 V with a current sink capability of at least 16 MA. "LS" stands for low-power Schottky.

■ ls-ttl unit load

a load with LS-TTL voltage levels, which will draw 20 μA for a logic 1 and -400 μA for a logic 0.

■ lubrication

in order to reduce wear and avoid overheating certain motor components require lubricating (application of an oil or grease). The bearings are the major motor component requiring lubrication (as per manufacturer's instructions). Excess greasing can however damage the windings and internal switches, etc.

■ luma

The brightness portion of a video signal ("Y").

■ luminescence

emission of light from a body when its atoms are excited by means other than raising its temperature. Short-lived luminescence is called fluorescence.

■ m

symbol for metre and milli- (thousandth).

■ M

symbol for mega (million).

■ MAC

Media Access Control

■ magnet wire

copper or aluminium wire with electrical insulating material applied to the surface to prevent continuity between adjacent turns in a winding.

■ magnetic amplifier

sometimes abbreviated 'Mag Amp,' a saturating inductor which is placed in series with a power supply output for regulation purposes.

■ magnetic energy

the product of the flux density (B) and the (de)magnetising force (H) in a magnetic circuit required to reach that flux density.

■ magnetic flux

a contrived but not measurable concept that has evolved in an attempt to describe the flow of a magnetic field. Unlike electric current where there is an actual flow of electrons, a magnetic field is the result of the energy state of a series of magnetic domains. Conceptually, one could imagine that the sequential change of energy state as the result of an applied field represents flow.

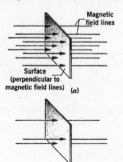

■ magnetic induction

the process of setting up magnetism in an object that is placed in a magnetic field.

■ magnetic lines of force

an imaginary line representing a magnetic field, which at every point has the direction of the magnetic flux at that point.

■ magnetic low-voltage

magnetic low-voltage lighting uses a magnetic (core and coil technology) transformer to convert normal line voltage (120 VAC) to low voltage (typically 12 VAC). This lower voltage is then used to power an incandescent low-voltage lamp. Only use a dimmer specifically designed for a magnetic low-voltage transformer.

■ magnetic path

the route the magnetic flux flows in a magnetic circuit.

■ magnetic path length

the length of the closed path that magnetic flux follows around a magnetic circuit. Amperes Law determines it.

■ magnetic polarity

it is a fundamental principle of a

winding that adjacent poles must be wound to give opposite magnetic polarity. This does not mean that the coils actually have to be wound in this direction before being placed into the stator. It does mean that the winding must be connected so that, if the current proceeds through one pole in a clockwise direction, it must proceed through the next pole in a counterclockwise direction. This principle is used to determine the correctness of connection diagrams.

magnetic wire

wire used to create a magnetic field such as those in magnetic components (inductors and transformers). Magnet wire is nearly 100% copper and must be made from virgin copper. It is covered with a number of difference organic polymer film coatings.

magnetism

phenomena associated with magnetic fields. Magnetic fields are produced by moving charged particles: in electromagnets, electrons flow through a coil of wire connected to a battery; in permanent magnets, spinning electrons within the atoms generate the field.

mainframe

a unit which accepts modules and/ or cards. Typically in Universal Switching's equipment, the Mainframe unit provides control and power to the modules installed.

mains

source of electrical power, normally the electricity supply system.

mains frequency

electricity ac supply frequency; 50 Hz in India.

majority carriers

the type of current carriers, free electrons or holes, of which a given semiconductor contains the most.

mandrel

a fiber wrapping device used to cause attenuation within a fiber cable.

margining

adjusting a power supply output voltage up or down from its minimal setting in order to verify system performance margin with respect to supply voltage. This is usually done electrically by a system-generated control signal.

master / master mainframe

a mainframe that has control of other mainframes (slaves) in a serial chain. A master/slave combination has one bus address and appears as one mainframe with increased capacity.

master/slave operation

wire used to create a magnetic field such as those in magnetic components (inductors and transformers). Magnet wire is nearly 100% copper and must be made from virgin copper. It is covered with a number of difference organic polymer film coatings.

matrix

an arrangement of signal circuits

in which input buses are represented by parallel vertical lines and output buses as overlapping horizontal lines (or visa versa), forming a grid-like array. Crosspoint switches at each crossing point connect inputs to outputs. Also referred to as a switching array, or crosspoint switch.

■ **maximum ambient operating temperature**

the highest ambient temperature at which a circuit is expected to operate.

■ **maximum device voltage**

the highest voltage that can safely be dropped across a polyswitch device in its tripped state under specified fault conditions. Synonyms: Maximum Interrupt Voltage,Maximum Voltage,Vmax

■ **maximum fault current**

the rated maximum value of peak pulse current of specified amplitude and wave shape that may be applied without damage.

■ **maximum interrupt current**

the highest fault current that can safely be used to trip a polyswitch device under specified conditions. Typically the lower the voltage dropped across the polyswitch device in its tripped state, the higher the maximum interrupt current. Maximum interrupt currents are usually shown in this databook at the maximum voltage. It may be possible to use a polyswitch device at a higher interrupt current, but each such use must be individually qualified. Synonyms: Imax

■ **maximum interrupt voltage**

the highest voltage that can safely be dropped across a polyswitch device in its tripped state under specified fault conditions. Synonyms: Maximum Device Voltage,Maximum Voltage,Vmax

■ **maximum load**

highest amount of output load allowable under the continuous operating specifications of a converter.

■ **maximum operating voltage**

the maximum voltage across a polyswitch device under a typical fault condition. In many circuits, this is the voltage of the power source in the circuit. It may be possible to use a polyswitch device at a higher voltage, but each such use must be individually qualified.

■ **maximum output resistance**

the resistance of a device at a specified voltage.

■ **maximum power dissipation**

an inductor's ability to handle the heat generated by operating at maximum current at an ambient temperature, expressed in Watts (W) or milliwatts (mW). This is a function of the body area of the inductor, core material used, and varies for shielded vs. unshielded.

■ **maximum resistance**

the maximum resistance of a polyswitch device at room temperature one hour after being tripped or after reflow soldering.

Synonyms: R1max

maximum switching current

the maximum current that a device switches at safely without damage.

maximum voltage

the highest voltage that can safely be dropped across a polyswitch device in its tripped state under specified fault conditions. Synonyms: Maximum Device Voltage, Maximum Interrupt Voltage, Vmax

maxwell

the unit of magnetic flux in the CGS system. One Maxwell = 10^{-8} webers.

MBPS

Megabits Per Second (millions of bits per second). A measure of digital data transmission rate.

MCNS

Multimedia Cable Network System

MDU

Multi-Dwelling Unit

mean time between failure (mtbf)

unit of measure, expressed in hours, that gives the relative reliability of a converter. MTBF data is based upson actual operating data (demonstrated) or derived per the conditions of MIL-HDBK-217F (calculated).

measuring system

consists of an encoder and associated electronics incorporating interpolation, counter, readout and/or data interface.

mechanical splice (fiber optic)

a mechanical means of connecting two fibers.

medium motors

motors in NEMA 143T to 449T frames.

mega

a prefix, abbreviated "M," used to denote units of millions, 10^6. One "Mega" is equal to one million. In our industry, one Mega hertz is a frequency of one million hertz (cycles per second).

megaohm

a unit of electrical resistamce equal to one million ohms.

megaohmmeter

an instrument for measuring extremely high resistance.

megawatt

a unit of power equal to one million watts. Put another way, it's the amount of electric energy required to light 10,000 10-watt bulbs.

megawatt-hour (mWh)

one million watts used for one hour. If you purchased a megawatt-hour of energy for a nickel per kilowatt-hour, it would cost you 1,000 nickels, or Rs. 50.00. Using a kWh your could burn one, 100-watt incandescent for 24 hours a day for about 14 months, or 3 hours a day for over 9 years.

■ **meggar test**

a measure of an insulation system's resistance. This is usually measured in megohms and tested by passing a high voltage at low current through the motor windings and measuring the resistance of the various insulation systems.

■ **megger**

a test instrument fpr measuring the insulation resistance of conductors and other electrical equipment; specifically, a megaohm (million ohms) meter; this is a registered trade mark of the James Biddle Co.

■ **mercaptan**

a highly concentrated odorant that is injected into natural gas before it enters a utilities distribution system. Mercaptan gives off a foul smell, reminiscent of rotten eggs.

■ **mercury wetted relay**

a reed relay in which the contacts are wetted by a film of mercury (Hg). Usually has a required operating position to avoid liquid mercury from shorting the contacts; other types are position insensitive. This type of relay is usually higher power and longer life, but at a higher dollar cost. Another benefit of this type of contact is the repeatability of contact resistance and virtually no contact bounce.

■ **MES**

Manufacturing Execution System.

■ **methane (CH4)**

derived from the Greek word "methy" meaning wine. The early Greeks believed if they drank wine from cups carved from the crystal amethyst they could not become intoxicated (Greek "methyein").

Methane is a simple hydrocarbon composed of one carbon atom surrounded by four hydrogen atoms. It is an odorless, flammable and invisible gas and the primary ingredient in natural gas. Natural gas companies add a strong odorant to the gas for safety so it can be easily detected by smelling. Methane is a relatively clean fuel and it is commonly used to fuel vehicles in many countries, such as New Zealand and Italy.

■ **metre**

the SI fundamental unit of length, equal to 1.093 yards. (Meter in US.)

■ **metropolitan area network (man)**

a data communication network covering the geographic area of a city. Often used by a CAP to carry backbone traffic in their serving area.

■ **MHz**

the abbreviation for "MegaHertz," used to describe the frequency of a crystal or oscillator in terms of millions of Hertz (cycles per second). A frequency specified as "10.0 MHz" would be understood as being a frequency of 10,000,000 Hertz (cycles per second).

■ **milli**

a prefix, abbreviated "m," used to

denote units of thousandths, 10^{-3}. One "milli" is equal to 1/1000th of a unit.

MIMO

Multiple-Input Multiple-Output.

minimum load

the minimum load current/power that must be drawn from the power supply in order for the supply to meet its performance specifications. Less frequently, a minimum load is required to prevent the power from failing.

minimum operating temperature

minimum ambient temperature at which a converter will start and operate within specifications.

minimum phase system

a system whose poles and zeros lie in the open left half plane. The idea is that such poles and zeros are associated with first quadrant phase plots. See **bode plot**.

minority carriers

the type of current carriers, free electrons or holes, of which a given semiconductor contains the least.

MIS

Manufacturing Information System.

MLT

the Mean-Length-Turn of wire for a core.

mmds

Multi-channel, Multipoint Distribution Service

MMI

man Machine Interface. Also known as human machine interface. The communication between the computer system and the people who use it.

modal controllability

it can be shown that an LTI system (A,B,C,D) is controllable if and only if each of its modes are controllable. A mode (eigenvalue) is controllable if a control can be constructed to move the system's state anywhere along the associated eigenvector. If this is not possible, we say that the mode is uncontrollable. Also see **controllability** and **stabilisability**.

modbus

an industrial networking system that uses peer-to-peer communications.

modem

an acronym for MOdulator/DEModulator. Modems are data communications devices that convert digital signals to analog signals for transmission over analog public telephone networks.

modular

a physically descriptive term used to describe a power supply made up of a number of separate subsections, such as an input module, power module, or filter module. Modular construction tends to lower the MTBF.

modular angle encoder

angle encoder, consisting essentially of disk and scanning unit assemblies (rotor and stator) which are integrated into a machine or a rotary table.

■ **modular jack**

the female connector used at the end of each horizontal cabling drop. Usually Modular Jacks utilise a 6 or 8 contact modular plug (on the patching side) and a 110, Krone, or other Insulation Displacement connection method (on the permanent horizontal wiring side).

■ **modular plug**

the male connector usually found at the end of a patch cord.

■ **modulation**

process by which signal characteristics are transformed to represent information. Types of modulation include frequency modulation (FM), where signals of different frequencies represent different data values.

■ **module**

encapsulated DC-DC converter.

■ **Moire principle**

photoelectric scanning method to produce periodic signals using two fine gratings which are closely positioned to each other and have approximately parallel and equally spaced lines.

■ **MOM**

Message-Oriented Middleware

■ **motional capacitance**

a parameter associated with a quartz crystal unit, used to illustrate the electronic equivalence of the mechanical elasticity of the unit. Motional capacitance may be abbreviated as "Cm" or "C1."

■ **motional inductance**

a parameter associated with a quartz crystal unit, used to illustrate the electronic equivalence of the mechanical mass of the unit. Motional inductance may be abbreviated as "Lm" or "L1."

■ **motor**

a device that takes electrical energy and converts it into mechanical energy to turn a shaft.

■ **MPLS**

Multi-Protocol Label Switching

■ **mpp core**

MPP is an acronym for Molypermalloy Powder. It is a magnetic material that has an inherent distributed air gap. The distributed air gap allows the core to store higher levels of magnetic flux when compared to other magnetic materials such as ferrite. This characteristic allows a higher DC current level to flow through the inductor before is saturates. The basic raw materials are nickel, iron, and molybdenum. The ratios are approximately 80% nickel, 2-3% molybdenum, and 17-18% iron. The manufacturing process includes an annealing step as discussed in the Kool Mu˝ definition. MPP stores higher amounts of energy and has a higher permeability than Kool Mu˝. Cores are offered in 10 or more permeability selections. The core characteristics allow inductors to perform very well in switching power applications. Since the core can store higher energy, more DC current can be passed through the inductor before the core reaches saturation. However, the cost of MPP is significantly higher than Kool Mu, iron powder, and most ferrite.

■ MTBF

(Mean Time Between Failures) may be calculated or demonstrated. The usual calculation is per Mil-Std 217 rev E. Demonstrated reliability is usually determined by temperature accelerated life testing. Demonstrated MTBF is almost always greater than calculated MTBF.

■ MTTR

an abbreviation for Mean Time To Repair, a theoretical period of time need to repair a piece of equipment given certain circumstances.

■ MTU

Multi-Tenant Unit

■ multifilar winding

a winding technique in which a single turn consists of two or more strands of magnetwire operating in parallel. This reduces some of the second order effects associated with a single strand of wire, including skin effect downfalls and winding ease.

■ multi-level

usually indicating that separate levels of switching are included different levels are required. This is typical when switching RS-232

type data lines. These could be up to 25 levels deep. Some types of video signals are divided into different levels, one for each primary colour (Red, Green and Blue). For most applications of this nature, this type of switching array is gang controlled.

■ multi-location dimming

allows full-range dimming from two to ten locations.

■ multimode

A type of fiber optic cable where the core diameter is much larger than the wavelength of light transmitted. Two common multimode fiber types are 50/125 and 62.5/125.

■ multiplexer(mux)

1) a technique that enables several data streams to be sent over a single physical line. It is also a function by which one connection from a layer is used to support more than one connection to the next higher layer.

2) a device for combining several channels to be carried by one line or fiber.

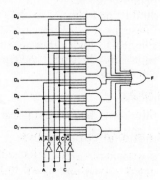

■ multiplexing

where each signal is switched in turn to a single analogue-to-digital converter. As opposed to where one A-D converter is used for each signal in simultaneous sampling.

■ multi-speed motors

a motor wound in such a way that varying connections at the starter can change the speed to a predetermined speed. The most common multi-speed motor is a two speed although three- and four-speeds are sometimes available. Multi-speed motors can be wound with two sets of windings or one winding. They are also available either constant torque, variable torque or constant horsepower.

■ multiturn rotary encoder

absolute rotary encoder which determines the angular position of the shaft and the number of shaft rotations.

■ municipal utility

(Municipally owned electric system) a utility that is owned and operated by a city. In most cases, municipal utility rates are set at the city level, either by the municipal administration or by a local utility board or commission. In some limited circumstances, state-level regulation applies. Municipal utilities often have access to low-cost power from federal hydroelectric projects and can obtain low interest loans, and they are exempt from income and other taxes at the federal and state levels. These factors contribute to lower financing costs for plant and equipment. Municipal utilities serve roughly 14 percent of the nation's electric consumers.

■ mutual inductance (m)

the ability of one conductor to induce an emf in a nearby conductor when the current in the first conductor changes.

■ mutual induction

the electromagnetic induction produced by one conductor in another nearby conductor, due to the moving flux of the first circuit cutting the conductors of the second circuit.

■ m x n

this term is another way to express a type of switching configuration. It is the same as a matrix or crosspoint switch where a number of inputs (M) can connect to a number of outputs (N). This term is common since when giving the dimensions of a matrix, it is usually is expressed as the number of input (M) by the number of outputs (N). For example, a matrix with 8 inputs and 32 outputs would commonly be expressed as an 8x32 matrix. The MxN term is also used since it doesn't explicitly indicate 'in' and 'out' since some type of matrices are bi-directional. When one axis has only a single port, this is commonly expressed as a 1xN array.

■ n

1 Redundancy

■ NAT

Network Address Translation

■ **natural gas**

mixture of flammable gases found in the Earth's crust (often in association with petroleum), now one of the world's three main fossil fuels (with coal and oil). Natural gas is a mixture of hydrocarbons, chiefly methane, with ethane, butane and propane.

■ **NCC**

Network Control Centre

■ **NDIS**

Network Drive Interface Specification

■ **network**

the physical interconnection of devices sharing a communications protocol.

■ **network interface card (nic)**

network devices that are installed in computers so that they can be connected to a network. Ethernet NICs come in different speeds as well as with connections to different media types.

■ **network management system**

a system responsible for managing at least part of a network. NMSs communicate with agents to help keep track of network statistics and resources.

■ **neutron**

one of the three chief sub-atomic particles (the others being the proton and the electron). Neutrons have about the same mass as protons but no electric charge, and occur in the nuclei of all atoms except hydrogen. They contribute to the mass of atoms but do not affect their chemistry, which depends on the proton or electron numbers. For instance, isotopes of a single element (with different masses) differ only in the number of neutrons in their nuclei and have identical chemical properties.

■ **no load loss (core losses)**

these losses are caused by the magnetising of the core and are always present. The way they are measured is by running full voltage with no load on the transformer

■ **no load voltage**

voltage level present at the output pins of a converter when 0% load is applied.

■ **NOC**

Network Operations Centre

■ **node**

a device with a direct point of access to a network.

■ **noise**

any unwanted electrical signals contaminating the signal to be measured. This noise may be electronic noise which is an artefact of semiconductor construction techniques and is not reducible. alternatively the noise may be caused by environmental factors. This type of noise can be the result of poor positioning or screening of signal wiring. This may result in mains frequency or RF pickup contaminating the required signal.

noise attenuation

refers to the ability of a feedback system to attenuate noise (typically sensor noise). Typically, it is desirable for feedback systems to attenuate/reject high frequency sensor noise.

noise figure

an expression of noise generated with in a device specified in dB. This parameter is important in RF application such as a receive antenna switching system and IF signal routing. The lower the noise figure, the better.

nominal model

refers to a mathematical model which approximates (usually accurately) a given system. An engineer may, for example, neglect high frequency dynamics in situations which require low frequency operation. Care must always be taken in making such approximations.

nominal value

ideal value that is used as a reference point. Typically, it is not the same as the value actually measured.

nonautomatic substation

indicates that the substation equipment will not function unless manually initiated by an operator.

non-blocking

a term with multiple and conflicting industry usage. 1) May be used to express the ability to connect a single input of a switching array to multiple outputs simultaneously without any input loading or mis-matches. This usually results in a constant signal loss because of the use of power dividers (signal splitters) to configure the non-blocking switching array. Non-blocking switching arrays can also be achieved using impedance shifting in place of power dividers. Also referred to as Full Fanout. 2) In multi-stage switching arrays (tri-stage or 3-stage), it refers to the ability to route and input to an output at all times (no blocking due to unavailable middle stages).

non-conforming

a product outside manufacturing limits but not necessarily defective.

non-destructive testing

method of inspecting materials and products without affecting their subsequent properties and performance. Abbreviation NDT.

noninductive circuit

a circuit in which the magnetic effect of the current flowing has been reduced by one several methods to a minimum or to zero.

nonlinear load

a load where the wave shape of the steady state current does not follow the wave shape of the applied voltage.

nonlinear material

magnetic material that exhibits a permeability which changes dramatically when MMF is varied.

non-minimum phase system

refers to systems which have at least one pole and/or zero in the closed right half plane. Usually this term is used to refer to systems which possess zeros in the open right half plane.

non-renewable energy

an electricity-generating source that can only be used once, such as oil, coal, natural gas and nuclear energy.

normal operating current

the highest steady state current that is expected to flow in a circuit under normal operating conditions. At the maximum ambient operating temperature of the circuit, the hold current of a polyswitch device used to protect the circuit is typically greater than the normal operating current.

normal value

a usual, average, normal, or expected operating condition. This stated value will probably not be equal to the value actually measured.

NTSC

National Television Standards Committee. This Organisation developed the original NTSC standard for colour television used in North America, Japan and many other countries.

n-type connector

a larger threaded coaxial connector with high power handling and good high frequency characteristics. Typically usable to 12.5 GHz, but some manufacturers offer connectors usable to 18 GHz.

n-type semiconductor

a doped semiconductor in which the majority current carriers are electrons.

n-type thermocouple

nicrosil-Nisil thermocouple with a temperature range of -200 to 1200 °C.

nuclear energy

energy from the inner core or nucleus of the atom, as opposed to energy released in chemical processes, which is derived from the electrons surrounding the nuclei. Nuclear fusion is the release of thermonuclear energy by the conversion of hydrogen nuclei to helium nuclei, in a continuing reaction in the Sun and other stars. Nuclear fusion is the principle behind thermonuclear weapons (the hydrogen bomb). Attempts to harness fusion for commercial power production have so far not succeeded.

nuclear fission

process whereby an atomic nucleus breaks up into two or more major fragments with the emission of two or three neutrons. It is accompanied by the release of energy in the form of gamma radiation and the kinetic energy of the emitted particles.

nuclear fusion

process where two atomic nuclei are fused, with the release of a large amount of energy. Very high temperatures and pressures are required for the fusion. Under these conditions the atoms involved are stripped of all their electrons so that the remaining particles, which together make up plasma, can come close together at very high speeds and overcome the mutual repulsion of the positive charges on the atomic nuclei. At very close range another nuclear force will come into play, fusing the particles together to form a larger nucleus. As fusion is accompanied by the release of large amounts of energy, the process might one day be harnessed to form the basis of commercial energy production. Methods of achieving controlled fusion are therefore the subject of research around the world.

■ **nuclear waste**

the radioactive and toxic byproducts of the nuclear-energy and nuclear-weapons industries. Nuclear waste may have an active life of several thousand years. Disposal, by burial on land or at sea, has raised problems of safety, environmental pollution, and security. In absolute terms, nuclear waste cannot be safely relocated or disposed of.

■ **nucleus**

in physics, the positively charged central part of an atom, which constitutes almost all its mass. Except for hydrogen nuclei, which have only protons, nuclei are composed of both protons and neutrons. Surrounding the nucleus are electrons, which contain a negative charge equal to the protons, thus giving the atom a neutral charge.

■ **Nyquist frequency**

if an analog signal is sampled at a rate more than twice that of its highest frequency component, it can be properly reconstructed when reconverted back to the analog domain. The required sampling rate is called the Nyquist frequency. Conversely, the analog bandwidth required to accurately transmit a properly reconstructed sampled image is one half the image sample (pixel clock) rate.

■ **Nyquist theorem**

the Nyquist theorem demands that a signal be sampled at at least twice its maximum frequency. To get an accurate picture of a waveform however, a sampling rate of 10 - 20 times the highest frequency is better.

■ **obligation to serve**

the responsibility of a regulated utility, under traditional regulation, to provide service to all consumers in its service territory on a nondiscriminatory basis. This means that utilities must build, operate and maintain generating plants and transmission and distribution systems to serve all their present and future consumers.

■ **observability**

refers to the ability or inability to uniquely reconstruct (estimate) the state of a system in finite time given output and input measurements. If the state can be determined uniquely in finite time, then we say that the system is observable. If not, we say that the system is unobservable. Also see **the** dual concept of controllability.

observer

a model based filter which is used to reconstruct (or estimate) the state of a system from knowledge of noisy output and input measurements. Also called a State Estimator and Kalman Filter.

OD

Outside Diameter.

OEM

Original Equipment Manufacturer. A company which makes basic computer hardware for other manufacturers to build into their products.

oersted

the unit of magnetic field strength (H) in the CGS system. One Oersted equals the magnetomotive force of one Gilbert per centimeter of flux path.

off line

a power supply which receives its input power from the AC line, without using a 50/60 Hz power transformer prior to rectification and filtering, hence the term off line power supply.

off-line power supply

power supply (linear or switching) that operates directly off the AC line. The input voltage is rectified and filtered prior to any isolation transformer.

offset error

if you get a reading other than zero for a zero condition then you have an offset error: every reading will be inaccurate by this amount.

off-state capacitance

capacitance in the off-state measured at a specified frequency, amplitude, and DC bias.

off-state current

dC value of the current through a SiBar device that results from the application of the off-state voltage, VD. IDM designates the maximum off-state current.

off-state voltage

dC voltage when a SiBar device is in the off-state. VDM designates the maximum off-state voltage.

ohm

sI unit of resistance, such that one ampere through it produces a potential difference of one voltage.

ohmmeter

an instrument for measuring resistance in ohms. Take a look at this diagram to see how an ohmmeter is used to check a small control transformer. The ohmmeter's pointer deflection is controlled by the amount of battery current passing through the moving coil. Before measuring the resistance of an unknown resistor or electrical circuit, the ohmmeter must first be calibrated. If the value of resistance to be measured can be estimated within reasonable limits, a range selected that will give approximately half-scale deflection when the resistance is inserted between the probes. If the resistance is unknown, the selector switch is set on the highest scale. Whatever range is selected, the meter must be calibrated to read zero before the unknown resistance is measured.

■ **oil**

Flammable substance, usually soluble in water, and composed chiefly of carbon and hydrogen. Oils may be solids (fats and waxes) or liquids. The three main types are: essential oils, obtained from plants; fixed oils, obtained from animals and plants; and mineral oils, obtained chiefly from the refining of petroleum.'

■ **oil circuit breaker**

a device that opens an alternating current circuit in a tank of oil which extinguishes the arc. It is also called an oil switch.

■ **oil mist lubrication-dry sump**

a method for lubricating anti-friction bearings which utilises oil dispersed on an air stream. The mist is exhausted from the bearing housing so as not to permit oil to accumulate.

■ **oil mist lubrication-wet sump**

similar to Oil Mist Lubrication - Dry Sump, except that a pool of oil is developed in the bearing chamber. This oil pool will continue to supply oil to the bearing in the event that the oil mist is interrupted and is fed from a source outside the bearing housing such as a constant level oiler.

■ **on-off control**

a simple control system which is either on or off.

■ **on-state current**

current through a SiBar device in the on-state condition IT.

■ **on-state voltage**

voltage across a SiBar device in the on-state condition at a specified current, IT.

■ **open (protected) motor**

a motor having ventilating openings which permit passage of external cooling air over and around the windings. The term 'open machine', when applied to large apparatus without qualification, designates a machine having no restriction to ventilation other than that necessitated by mechanical construction.

■ **open bearing**

a ball bearing that does not have a shield, seal or guard on either of the two sides of the bearing casing.

■ **open circuit inductance**

the inductance measured at the winding of a transformer at a low flux density level.

■ **open externally-ventilated machine**

a machine which is ventilated with external air by means of a separate motor-driven blower mounted on machine enclosure.

■ **open frame**

a power supply where there is no external metal chassis; the power supply is provided to the end user essentially as a printed circuit board which provides mechanical support as well as supporting the components and making electrical connections.

open loop poles

refers to poles (finite or at infinity) of the open loop transfer function.

open loop zeros

refers to zeros (finite or at infinity) of the open loop transfer function.

open pipe-ventilated machine

an open machine except that openings for admission of ventilating air are so arranged that inlet ducts or pipes can be connected to them. Air may be circulated by means integral with machine or by means external to and not a part of the machine. In the latter case, this machine is sometimes known as separately- or force-ventilated machine.

open right half plane

refers to all points in the complex s-plane which possess a real part which is strictly negative.

open systems interconnection

a 7-layer architecture model for communications systems developed by ISO and used as a reference model for most network architectures.

open-circuit voltage

see no load voltage.

operating range current

the range of normal operating currents in a circuit containing a polyswitch device. Typically the hold current of the polyswitch device should be greater than the top of the operating current range.

operating reserves

operating reserves are the amount of electricity generation that is available in excess of current demand.

operating temperature range

range of ambient temperatures over which a component can be operated safely. The operating temperature is different from the storage temperature in that it accounts for the component's self temperature rise caused by the winding loss from a given DC bias current. This power loss is referred to as the copper loss and is equal to: Power Loss=$(DCR)(1^2)dc$This power loss results in an increase to the component temperature above the given ambient temperature. Thus, the maximum operating temperature will be less than the maximum storage temperature: Maximum Operating Temperature = Storage Temperature - Self Temperature Rise

operator

a mathematical object which maps functions to functions. A system is an example of an operator. Extends the concept of a function.

optoisolator

an electro-optical device which

transmits a signal across a DC isolation boundary.

■ oscillation mode

a quartz crystal is designed to vibrate on its fundamental frequency or one of its overtones. This becomes important between the 24MHz to 40MHz range. Crystals in that frequency range may be made as either a high fundamental or a low 3rd overtone. Fundamental mode crystals at these frequencies become more expensive, because the quartz blank is extremely thin, difficult to handle, and subject to a higher rate of breakage in processing. If you are able to use the 3rd overtone crystal instead of the fundamental, your cost savings may be significant. As the frequency range is extended, the oscillation mode of the crystal changes to other overtones. Crystals in the range of 60-110MHz are generally 5th overtones, while crystals in the range of 110-175MHz generally are 7th overtones.

■ oscillator

a circuit or device that produces an alternating current of a specific frequency at its output terminals.

■ OSS

Operational Support System

■ outlet

place to plug in appliances and other devices that operate on electricity.

■ output

information leaving a device.

■ output bus

an output circuit path leading from the output(s) of one or more crosspoint switches arranged in a crosspoint switching array. Typically, only one crosspoint switch at a time can feed a signal to an output bus. Each output connector is fed from an output bus.

■ output current

is represented by I_{OL} and I_{OH}, which is the output current at V_{OL} and V_{OH}.

■ output current limiting

see **current limiting** and **foldback current limiting**.

■ output filter

a low pass filter placed in the output of the rectified power converter to minimise (or smooth) the square wave or sine wave output of the converter. This filter has an LC,RC or Pi configuration.

■ output good

a power supply status signal which indicates that the output voltage is within a certain tolerance. An output which is either too high or too low will deactivate the Output Good signal.

■ output impedance

ratio of change in output voltage to a change in output load current. Sometimes referred to as Dynamic Response.

■ output load (fan out)

the capacity of the oscillator to drive other devices. TTL devices are specified in the number of gates that can be driven; i.e., 10 TTL gates. CMOS outputs are specified in picoFarads (pF); i.e., 15pF or 50pF loads.

■ **output noise**

the AC component that may be present on the DC output of a power supply. Switch-mode power supply output noise has two components: a lower frequency component at the switching frequency of the converter and a high frequency component due to fast edges of the converter switching transitions. Noise should always be measured directly at the output terminals with a scope probe having an extremely short grounding lead.

■ **output ripple and noise**

see **noise and periodic and random distribution.**

■ **output voltage**

is represented by V_{OL} which is the maximum voltage that output low will be and V_{OH} which is the minimum voltage that output high will be.

■ **output voltage accuracy**

maximum allowable deviation of the DC output of a converter from its ideal or nominal value. Expressed as a percentage of output voltage. Often called output voltage tolerance

■ **output voltage range**

minimum and maximum output voltage limits within which a converter meets its operating specifications.

■ **overcurrent**

any current in excess of the rated current of equipment or the ampacity of a conductor. It may result from overload, short circuit or ground fault.

■ **overcurrent protection**

output monitoring circuit activated if the converter exceeds a preset current level.

■ **overdamped poles**

refers to distinct real poles which are stable (i.e. lie in the open left half plane). Such poles have a damping ratio zeta which lies in the interval (1, infinity) and are associated with decaying exponentials in the time domain.

■ **overlap time**

the time, measured at 50% Vp-p, at which the two outputs of a complementary output ECL oscillator overlap.

■ **overload**

load greater than the load for which the system or mechanism was intended. A fault, such as a short circuit or ground fault, is not an overload.

■ **overload protection**

a power supply protection circuit that limits the output current under overload conditions.

■ **overload relay**

relay that senses an overload on lines or apparatus and initiates the opening.

■ **overshoot**

a transient output voltage change

which exceeds the high limit of the voltage accuracy specification and is caused by turning the power supply on or off, or abruptly changing line or load conditions.

■ **overtemp warning**

a TTL compatible signal which indicates that an overtemperature condition exists in the power supply. Most commercial power supplies are designed to shut down if an overtemperature condition exists.

■ **overtemperature protection**

design feature that protects the silicon die from exceeding its designed operating temperature range. The device will thermally cycle until the abnormal condition is corrected.

■ **overtone**

an odd numbered multiple of the fundamental frequency.

■ **overvoltage lockout**

design feature that protects the silicon die and downstream peripherals from supply voltage conditions that exceed its operating voltage limits. Raychem power switches have a nominal OVLO threshold of 6.4V. Synonyms: OVLO

■ **Over Voltage Protection (OVP)**

output monitoring circuit activated if a preset voltage level is exceeded. Depending on the type of circuit used, the OVP shuts the converter down, "crowbars" the faulty output or switches the converter to a different operating mode.

■ **ovlo**

design feature that protects the silicon die and downstream peripherals from supply voltage conditions that exceed its operating voltage limits. Raychem power switches have a nominal OVLO threshold of 6.4V.

■ **OXC**

Optical Cross-connect

■ **ozone**

O_3 highly reactive pale-blue gas with a penetrating odor. Ozone is an allotrope of oxygen made up of three atoms of oxygen. It is formed when the molecule of the stable form of oxygen (O2) is split by ultraviolet radiation or electrical discharge. It forms a thin layer in the upper atmosphere, which protects life on Earth from ultraviolet rays, a cause of skin cancer. At lower atmosphere levels it is an air pollutant and contributes to the greenhouse effect.

■ **P base**

a special mounting similar to "D" flange except with a machine fit tenon recessed instead of protruding. Usually found on pumps.

■ **package**

physical holder of the crystal unit.

■ **packet**

1) a logical grouping of information that includes a header and (usually) user data. 2) Continuous sequence of binary digits of information is switched through the network and an integral unit.

packet switched network

a network in which data is transmitted in units called packets. The packets can be routed individually over the best available network connection and reassembled to form a complete message at the destination.

pair gain

the multiplexing of x phone conversations over a lesser number of physical capabilities. 'Pair gain' is the number of conversations obtained, divided by the number of wire pairs used by the systems.

PAN

Personal Area Network

panelboard

a single panel or group of panel units designed for assembly in the form of a single panel: includes buses and may come with or without switches and/or automatic overcurrent protective devices for the control of light, heat, or power circuits of individual as well as aggregate capacity. It is designed to be placed in a cabinet or cutout box that is in or against a wall or partition and is accessible only from the front.

parabolic temperature curve

BT-cut and Tuning Fork crystals frequencies follow a parabolic curve over temperature. The frequency will decrease as the temperature goes above or below the turnover temperature.

parallax

an optical illusion which occurs in analog meters and causes reading errors. It occurs when the viewing eye is not in the same plane, perpendicular to the meter face, as the indicating needle.

parallel operation

connecting the outputs of two or more power supplies with the same output voltage for the purpose of obtaining a higher output current. This requires power supplies specially designed for load sharing.

parallel operation

operating Mode in which two or more power supplies are connected in parallel. The output currents are summed together into a single load, providing a higher level of output power than that available from a single DC-DC. Parallel operation requires DC-DCs speed specifically designed to share loads. Also see **master-slave operation**.

parallel resonant

a parallel resonant oscillator circuit uses a crystal unit that is designed to operate with a specified value of load capacitance. This will result in a crystal frequency higher than the series resonant frequency, but lower than the true parallel resonant frequency. A basic parallel resonant circuit is illustrated below

parallel transmission

sending all data bits simultaneously. Commonly used for communications between computers and printer devices.

■ paralleling

when two or more DC motors are required to operate in parallel - that is, to drive a common load while sharing the load equally among all motors - they should have speed-torque characteristics which are identical. The greater the speed droop with load, the easier it becomes to parallel motors success-fully. It follows that series motors will operate in parallel easier than any other type. Compound motors, which also have drooping speed characteristics (high regulation), will generally parallel without special circuits or equalization. It may be difficult to operate shunt or stabilised-shunt motors in parallel because of their nearly constant speed characteristics. Modifications to the motor control must sometimes be made before these motors will parallel within satisfactory limits.

■ pard

periodic and random deviation, referring to the sum of all ripple and noise components on the DC output of a power supply, regardless of nature or source.

■ parity

a technique for testing transmitting data. Typically, a binary digit is added to the data to make the sum of all the digits of the binary data either always even (even parity) or always odd (odd parity).

■ part lights

same as **dead leg.**

■ part winding start motor

is arranged for starting by first energizing part of the primary winding and subsequently energising the remainder of this winding in one or more steps. The purpose is to reduce the initial value of the starting current drawn or the starting torque developed by the motor. A standard part winding start induction motor is arranged so that one-half of its primary winding can be energized initially and subsequently the remaining half can be energized, both halves then carrying the same current.

■ particulates

from the Latin word "partire" meaning to divide, distribute or "part of." Particulates can be suspended solids or liquids that include dust from automobile and truck brake linings, road grit, ash from factory smokestacks, some from home chimneys and aerosols. Particulates reduce visibility and can cause lung and eye damage, especially when combined with other pollutants such as sulphur oxides (SOx) and nitrous oxides (NOx). Many people with respiratory problems are unaware their breathing problems can result from particulate pollution.

■ passband

a frequency range in which attenuation is guaranteed to be equal to or less than a designated value in dB, typically 3 dB.

■ passive aging test

a test described in Raychems

PS300 publication in which the resistance of a polyswitch device at room temperature is measured before and after aging at an elevated temperature (e.g., 70¡C or 85¡C) for an extended time (e.g., 1000 hours).

■ **patch cord**

a cable assembly with modular plugs on each end. Used for patching equipment to the patch panel in the equipment room and also used to connect to phones and computers at the drop.

■ **patch panel**

The common cross connect method used inside an equipment room. Typical Patch Panels utilise 110 or Krone connectors (on the rear) to connect to the horizontal cabling and modular jacks on the front to connect to equipment via patch cords.

■ **path resistance**

the resistance of a complete signal path, including the switching element's contact resistance, any PC board circuit resistance and connector terminal resistance and or cabling.

■ **PC**

Personal Computer. Generally applied to computers conforming to the IBM designed architecture.

■ **PCI**

Peripheral Component Interconnect
a local bus standard developed by in 1992. PCI cards plug into your computer and are configured through software. They do not have jumpers or switches.

■ **PCMCIA**

Personal Computer Memory Card International Association
industry group that developed the specification for credit card-sized plug-in cards for laptop computers.

■ **PD**

the power (in watts) dissipated by a polyswitch device in its tripped state. The power dissipation is the product of the current flowing through the device and the voltage across the device, in the tripped state.

■ **peak inverse voltage**

in an electron tube, the maximum negative voltage that can be applied to the plate without danger of arc-over. In a semiconductor diode, the maximum reverse bias voltage that can be applied without reaching the zener (or breakdown) voltage.

■ **peak load**

the highest, load on an electrical system or generator, occurring during a particular period of time.

■ **peak on-state surge current**

current through the device in the on-state condition.

■ **peak power**

the absolute maximum output power that a power supply can produce without immediate damage. Peak power capability is typically well beyond the continuous reliable output power capability and should only be used infrequently.

■ **peak pulse current**

rated maximum value of peak pulse current of specified amplitude and waveshape.

■ **peak value**

the highest or maximum value of an alternation of alternating current or voltage. This peak value occurs twice during each cycle.

■ **peak-to-peak value**

the maximum voltage change occuring during one cycle of alternating voltage or current. The total amount of voltage between the positive peak and the negative peak of one cycle or twice the peak value.

■ **pecl logic**

abbreviation for Positive Emitter Coupled Logic, a very high speed digital technology. Also see ECL.

■ **peer to peer**

a network architecture where computers connect directly with other computers without the need for servers.

■ **peer-to-peer communication**

a communication between networked devices in which any device can initiate data transfer.

■ **peltier effect**

when a current flows through a thermocouple junction, heat will either be absorbed or evolved depending on the direction of current flow. This effect is independent of joule $I^2 R$ heating.

■ **percent ripple**

the percentage of ripple or AC flux to total flux, or in an inductor, the percentage of alternating current to average current.

■ **percent saturation**

the 100% permeability minus the percent of initial permeability. ie 20% saturation = 80% of initial permeability.

■ **perfectly balanced rotor**

a rotor is perfectly balanced when its mass distribution is such that it transmits no vibratory force or motion to its bearings as a result of centrifugal forces.

■ **periodic and random deviation (pard)**

noise and ripple voltage superimposed on a converter's DC output. Typically specified at full load, it is expressed in peak-to-peak or RMS volts over a given bandwidth.

■ **peripheral**

A device that is external to the CPU and main memory, i.e., printer, modem or terminal, but is connected by the appropriate electrical connections.

■ **permanent magnet**

an artificial magnet that retains its magnetism after the magnetising force has been removed. Steel, when properly processed, can be made into a permanent magnet.

■ **permanent magnet synchronous**

(Hysteresis Synchronous), a motor with magnets embedded into the rotor assembly, which enable the rotor to align itself with the rotating magnetic field of the stator. These motors have zero slip (constant speed with load) and provide higher torque, efficiency and draw less current than comparable reluctance synchronous motors.

■ Permanent Virtual Circuit (PVC)

a defined virtual link with fixed end-points that are set-up by the network manager. A single virtual path may support multiple PVCs.

■ permeability

the ratio of the changes in flux density to changes in the magnetising force. The permeability of a magnetic material is the characteristic that gives the core the ability to concentrate lines of magnetic flux. The core material, as well as the core geometry, affects the cores effective permeability. For a given core shape, size, and winding, higher permeability materials result in higher inductance values as opposed to lower permeability materials.

■ permeability (core)

the permeability of a magnetic core is the characteristic that gives the core the ability to concentrate lines of magnetic flux. The core material, as well as the core geometry, affect the core's effective permeability. For a given core shape, size and material, and a given winding, higher permeability magnet materials result in a

higher inductance values as opposed to lower permeability materials.

■ PF

the abbreviation for 'PicoFarad,' used to describe a fractional part 10^{-12} (one trillionth) of one Farad.

■ pH junctions

the Junction of a reference electrode or combination electrode is a permeable membrane through which the fill solution escapes (called the liquid junction).

■ pH(s) (standard pH scale)

the conventional standard pH scale established on the basis that an individual ionic activity coefficient can be calculated from the Debye-Huckel law for primary buffers.

■ phase

indicates the space relationships of windings and changing values of the recurring cycles of A.C. voltages and currents. Due to the positioning (or the phase relationship) of the windings, the various voltages and currents will not be similar in all aspects at any given instant. Each winding will lead or lag another, in position. Each voltage will lead or lag another voltage, in time. Each current will lead or lag another current, in time. The most common power supplies are either single (10) or three phase (with 120 electrical degrees between the 3 phases).

■ phase crossovers

see **imaginary crossvers**.

■ **phase difference**

The time expressed in degrees between the same reference point on two periodic waveforms.

■ **phase evaluation**

method of determining position by detecting the phase between alternating voltages having a slight variation in frequency.

■ **phase grating scale**

scale with step grating which diffracts the transmitted or reflected light into 2 or more orders.

■ **phase margin**

amount of phase lag which can be introduced into a feedback loop before the closed loop system goes unstable. See **gain margin** and **delay margin**. Phase margin by definition is measured at gain crossovers or gain crossover frequencies.

■ **phase proportioning**

a form of temperature control where the power supplied to the process is controlled by limiting the phase angle of the line voltage.

■ **phase target**

a visual marker or flag on the overcurrent relays indicating the relay has sensed a fault on that phase or phases.

■ **photovoltaic cells**

photovoltaic cells are used to directly convert solar radiation into electricity. Materials called semiconductors, usually made from pure silicon, transfer light energy (photons) into electrical energy in a process known as the photoelectric effect.

■ **pi&d**

piping and instrumentation diagram.

■ **pico**

a prefix used to describe a submultiple of a number. One pico is one trillionth, 10^{-12}, of a unit.

■ **pid**

proportional gain, integral action time and derivative action time. PID software, for example, compares an analogue input value with a set point and if there's a discrepancy outputs an appropriate analogue or digital control value, according the PID calculations.

■ **piezoelectric accelerometer**

a transducer that produces an electrical charge in direct proportion to the vibratory acceleration.

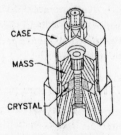

CASE

MASS

CRYSTAL

■ **piezoelectric currents**

the current caused by mechanical stress to the insulating materials or connectors. To minimise this problem in low current or voltage measurements, the stress must be removed from the insulators, and materials with a low piezoelectric effect must be used.

■ **piezoresistance**

Resistance that changes with stress.

■ **pi-filter**

a filter consisting of two capacitors connected in parallel with a series inductor. These filters are commonly found near DC-DC converters to filter ripple current and voltage.

■ **pin through**

refers to a package with leads. When the device is mounted on a PCB, the leads go through the board.

■ **pixel**

Picture element. Definable locations on a display screen that are used to form images on the screen. For graphic displays, screens with more pixels provide higher resolution.

■ **plane separation**

of a balancing machine, is the operation of reducing the correction plane interference ratio for a particular rotor.

■ **plant**

physical system to be controlled; system whose properties we want to alter via feedback.

■ **plate**

In an electron tube, the electrode that must be positive with respect to the cathode to allow the tube to conduct. Also called the Anode.

■ **plate current**

in an electron tube, the electron flow from cathode to plate. In the external plate circuit, the electron flow from the plate through the circuit, to the cathode.

■ **plate voltage**

in an electron tube, the difference of potential between plate and cathode.

■ **plates**

in a capacitor, the plates are the conducting surfaces.

■ **platinel**

a non-standard, high temperature platinum thermocouple alloy whose thermoelectric voltage nearly matches a Type K thermocouple (Trademark of Englehard Industries).

■ **platinum**

a noble metal which in its pure form is the negative wire of Type R and Type S thermocouples.

■ **platinum 10% rhodium**

the platinum-rhodium alloy used as the positive wire in conjunction with pure platinum to form a Type S thermocouple.

■ **platinum 13% rhodium**

the platinum-rhodium alloy used as the positive wire in conjunction with pure platinum to form a Type R thermocouple.

■ **platinum 30% rhodium**

the platinum-rhodium alloy used as the positive wire in conjunction with platinum 6% rhodium to form a Type B thermocouple.

■ platinum 6% rhodium

the platinum-rhodium alloy used as the negative wire in conjunction with platinum-30% rhodium to form a Type B thermocouple.

■ platinum 67

to develop thermal emf tables for thermocouples, the National Bureau of Standards paired each thermocouple alloy against a pure platinum wire (designated Platinum 2 prior to 1973, and currently Platinum 67). The thermal emf's of any alloy combination can be determined by summing the "vs. Pt-67" emf's of the alloys, i.e., the emf table for a Type K thermocouple is derived from the Chromel vs. Pt-67 and the Alumel vs. Pt-67 values.

■ PLC

Programmable Logic Controller.

■ plenum

chamber or space forming a part of an air conditioning system

■ plug

A popular term for a male gender connector of varied types.

■ plug reversal

reconnecting a motor's winding in reverse to apply a reverse braking torque to its normal direction of rotation while running. Although it is an effective dynamic braking means in many applications, plugging produces more heat than other methods and should be used with caution.

■ pn junction

a junction between an N-type semiconductor and a P-type semiconductor made by some method of diffusing, fusing or melting.

■ Poisson ratio

the ratio between the strain of expansion in the direction of force and the strain of contraction perpendicular to that force
$v = -Et/E1$.

■ polarisation

the inability of an electrode to reproduce a reading after a small electrical current has been passed through the membrane. Glass pH electrodes are especially prone to polarisation errors caused by small currents flowing from the pH meter input circuit and from static electrical charges built up as the electrodes are removed from the sample solution, or when the electrodes are wiped.

■ polarity

ability of a converter to produce an output that is positive or negative referenced to ground. Also see **floating output.**

■ polarisation test

a ratio of a one-minute meggar test (see **meggar test**) to ten-minute meggar test. Used to detect contaminants in winding insulation done typically on high voltage, V.P.I. motors which are tested by water immersion.

■ poles

in an AC motor, refers to the number of magnetic poles in the stator winding. The number of poles is a determinant of the motor's speed. (See Synchronous Speed)

In a DC motor, refers to the number of magnetic poles in the motor. Creates the magnetic field in which the armature operates. (Speed is not determined by the number of poles).

■ **polish**

a process used in the manufacture of some types of quartz crystals The polish process results in a very fine surface finish. The word 'polish' is also used to define the material used in the polish process, as well as the process itself.

■ **polyphase motor**

two or three-phase induction motors have their windings, one for each phase, evenly divided by the same number of electrical degrees. Reversal of the two-phase motor is accomplished by reversing the current through either winding. Reversal of a three-phase motor is accomplished by interchanging any two of its connections to the line. Polyphase motors are used where a polyphase (3-phase) power supply is available and is limited primarily to industrial applications. Starting and reversing torque characteristics of polyphase motors are exceptionally good. This is due to the fact that the different windings are identical and, unlike the capacitor motor, the currents are balanced. They have an ideal phase relation which results in a true rotating field over the full range of operation from locked rotor to full speed.

■ **pool pump program**

stigated to reduce system peak demand.

■ **POP**

Point Of Presence

■ **port**

a signal input (access) or output point on a computer.

■ **positive**

the point of any circuit from which the current flows. Opposite of negative.

■ **positive temperature coefficient**

a term used to describe a material whose resistivity increases as temperature increases. polyswitch devices make use of conductive polymers that show nonlinear PTC behavior. Synonyms: PTC

■ **post regulation**

output circuit that uses a linear regulator to prove line/load regulation and reduce ripple and noise. In PWM controlled converters, post regulation adds expense and degrades converter supply efficiency.

■ **post regulator**

a secondary regulating circuit on an auxiliary output of a power supply to provide full regulation on that output.

■ **post-reflow resistance**

the resistance of a polyswitch device at room temperature one hour after it has been connected to a circuit board by reflow soldering under specified conditions.

■ post-trip resistance

the resistance of a polyswitch device at room temperature one hour after the device has been tripped for the first time, under specified conditions.

■ potential

the pressure or voltage forcing electrical current through a circuit.

■ potential energy

the stored energy a body possesses because of its position with respect to other bodies. A stretched rubber band has potential energy. Gasoline in the liquid state has potential energy. When it is burned, it releases its chemical kinetic energy.

■ potential link

also known as a POT LINK. Device located in the meter to open the potential coil resulting in no disk rotation. Testing device.

■ potential, electric

in physics, the relative electrical state of an object. A charge conductor, for example, has a higher potential than the Earth, whose potential is taken by convention to be zero. An electric cell (battery) has a potential in relation to emf (electromotive force), which can make current flow in an external circuit. The difference in potential between two points — the potential difference — is expressed in volts; that is, a 12 V battery has a potential difference of 12 volts between its negative and positive terminals.

■ potentiometer

1. a variable resistor often used to control a circuit. 2. A balancing bridge used to measure voltage.

■ pothead

a device shaped like a pot or bell attached to the end of a cable which is used to attach the cable to a wire or overhead conductor.

■ powdered iron core

powdered iron is a magnetic material that has an inherent distributed air gap. The distributed air gap allows the core to store higher levels of magnetic flux when compared to other magnetic materials such as ferrites. This characteristic allows a higher DC current level to flow through the inductor before the inductor saturates. Powdered iron cores are made of nearly 100% iron. The iron particles are insulated form each other, mixed with a binder (such as phenolic or epoxy) and pressed into the final core shape. The cores are cured via a baking process. Other characteristics of powderded iron cores include: they are typically the lowest cost alternative and their permeabilities typically have a more stable temperature coefficient than ferrites (Also see **saturation current**)

■ power

the rate at which work is done or how much work is accomplished, divided by how long it took to do the work. The unit of power is the watt (W) or joule per second. If you lift a bean burrito above your head in one second, you have used about one watt of power. The word power is derived from the Latin word 'posse' meaning 'be able.'

power circuit breaker

this breaker will open the circuit under fault or overload conditions.

power code

identifies the type of power supply providing power to a DC motor. Frequency, voltage, and type of rectifier configuration.

power density

ratio of converter output power to converter volume.

power dissipation

the power (in watts) dissipated by a polyswitch device in its tripped state. The power dissipation is the product of the current flowing through the device and the voltage across the device, in the tripped state. Synonyms: Pd

power factor

a measurement of the time phase difference between the voltage and current in an AC circuit. It is represented by the cosine of the angle of this phase difference. For an angle of 0 degrees, the power factor is 100% and the volt/amperes of the circuit are equal to the watts. (This is the ideal and an unrealistic situation.) Power factor is the ratio of Real Power-KW to total KVA or the ratio of actual power (watts) to apparent power (volt-amperes).

power factor correction

design technique usually applied ot the input of off-line converters that improves the converter;s power factor and minimises harmonics generated by the converter onto the AC power line.

power fail

a power supply interface signal interface signal which gives a warning that the input voltage will no longer sustain full power regulated output.

power failure memory

circuitry that ensures that if lights are off when power fails, they will remain off when power is restored. If lights are on when power fails they will return to the previously set level when power is restored.

power good

signal (typically a visible LED) that indicates the DC output of the primary channel of a converter is still present.

power grid

a network of electric power lines and associated equipment used to transmit and distribute electricity over a geographic area.

power loss density (mw/ cm3)

the power absorbed by a body of ferromagnetic material and dissipated as heat.

power mosfet

semiconductor device used as a power switch in converters.

power rating

specified power available at the

converter output pins.

■ power source adjustment

a source of revenue based on the efficiency/inefficiency of customer equipment.

■ power supply

a separate unit or part of a circuit that supplies power to the rest of the circuit or to a system.

■ power switch

MOSFET-based switch that controls the flow of power through its output using an enable (EN) signal from a system controller. Advanced designs will include integrated pull-up resistors and capacitors to minimise board space and cost.

■ power transformer

magnetic-core transformer for operation at 60 hertz, with nearly zero source impedance, to transfer power from line voltage to some required voltage.

■ PPM

the abbreviation for "Parts Per Million," a method of calculation used to specify the permissible frequency deviation of a crystal or oscillator.

■ preload

a small amount of current drawn from a power supply to stabilise its operation. Preloads are usually provided by a bleeder resistor.

■ preset dimmer

preset dimmers have a built-in on/off switch that allows the user to turn lights on to a pre-selected light level.

■ primary

that winding of a transformer which is connected to and recieves energy from an external source of electrons. Also frequently referred to as the input winding.

■ primary circuits

input side of an isolated.

■ primary current

input side of an isolated DC-DC converter. See **secondary circuit**.

■ primary device

part of a flowmeter which is mounted internally or externally to the fluid conduit and produces a signal corresponding to the flowrate and from which the flow may be determined.

■ primary lines

high-voltage lines (4 kV, 6.9 W 12 kV, 16 kV, etc.) used to carry power from the substation to the immediate area to be transformed to lower voltages for individual customers.

■ primary standards

aqueous pH buffer solutions established by the National Bureau of Standards within the 2.5 to 11.5 pH range of ionic strength less than 0.1 and which provide stable liquid junction potential and uniformity of electrode sensitivity.

■ primary winding

that winding of a motor, transformer or other electrical device which is connected to the power source.

■ **prime mover**

an engine, turbine, or water wheel that drives or operates an electric generator.

■ **principal axes**

the axes of maximum and minimum normal stress.

■ **probe**

a generic term that is used to describe many types of temperature sensors.

■ **process meter**

a panel meter with sizeable zero and span adjustment capabilities, which can be scaled for readout in engineering units for signals such as 4-20 mA, 10-50 mA and 1-5 V.

■ **program**

a list of instructions that a computer follows to perform a task.

■ **prom**

programmable read-only memory. A semiconductor memory whose contents cannot be changed by the computer after it has been programmed.

■ **proof pressure**

the specified pressure which may be applied to the sensing element of a transducer without causing a permanent change in the output characteristics.

■ **propagation delay**

the specified amount of time for a signal to pass through a previously closed signal path. The delay must be considered, for example, when the signal is used to synchronise other signals, or is being used in a Clock / Data configuration. This is due to both the electrical length of the signal path, and any active components in the signal path.

■ **proportioning band**

a temperature band expressed in degrees within which a temperature controller's time proportioning function is active.

■ **proportioning control mode**

a time proportioning controller where the amount of time that the relay is energized is dependent upon the system's temperature.

■ **proportioning control plus derivative function**

a time proportioning controller with a derivative function. The derivative function senses the rate at which a system's temperature is either increasing or decreasing and adjusts the cycle time of the controller to minimise overshoot or undershoot.

■ **proportioning control plus integral**

a two-mode controller with time proportioning and integral (auto reset) action. The integral function automatically adjusts the temperature at which a system has stabilised back to the setpoint temperature, thereby eliminating droop in the system.

■ **proportioning control with integral and derivative functions**

three mode PID controller. A time proportioning controller with integral and derivative functions. The integral function automatically adjusts the system temperature to the set point temperature to eliminate droop due to the time proportioning function. The derivative function senses the rate of rise or fall of the system temperature and automatically adjusts the cycle time of the controller to minimise overshoot or undershoot.

■ **protection head**

an enclosure usually made out of metal at the end of a heater or probe where connections are made.

■ **protection tube**

a metal or ceramic tube, closed at one end into which a temperature sensor is inserted. The tube protects the sensor from the medium into which it is inserted.

■ **protective relay**

a relay, the principal function of which is to protect service from interruption, or to prevent or limit damage to apparatus.

■ **protocol**

a formal definition that describes how data is to be exchanged.

■ **psia**

pounds per square inch absolute. Pressure referenced to a vacuum.

■ **PSID**

Pounds per Square Inch Differential. Pressure difference between two points.

■ **PSIG**

Pound per Square Inch Gauge.

Pressure referenced to ambient air pressure.

■ **PSIS**

Pounds per Square Inch Standard. Pressure referenced to a standard atmosphere.

■ **PTC**

a term used to describe a material whose resistivity increases as temperature increases. polyswitch devices make use of conductive polymers that show nonlinear PTC behavior.

■ **p-type semiconductor**

a doped semiconductor in which the majority current carriers are holes.

■ **public utilities commission**

the state regulatory agency that governs retail utility rates and practices and, in many cases, issues approvals for the construction of new generation and transmission facilities. On average, roughly 90 percent of a utility's operations are regulated by the state commission.

■ **pullability**

the change in frequency of a crystal unit, either from the natural resonant frequency (Fr) to a load resonant frequency (FL), or from one load resonant frequency to another. The frequency can be pulled in a parallel resonant circuit by changing the value of load capacitance. A decrease in load capacitance causes an increase in frequency, and an increase in load capacitance causes a decrease in frequency.

■ **pull-up torque**

the minimum torque developed by an AC motor during the period of acceleration from zero to the speed at which breakdown occurs. For motors which do not have a definite breakdown torque, the pull-up torque is the minimum torque developed during the process of getting up to the rated speed.

R - R (r bar) is the per unit armature circuit resistance using counter emf as a base. Hot IR voltage drop = (Rated lax Hot Arm. Cir. Resistance) + 2.0 (Brush drop) volts.

■ **pulse**

a temporary change in voltage of any length.

■ **pulse transformers**

transformers designed for excitation that consists of short duration pulses repeated at a specific rate.

■ **Pulse Width Modulation (PWM)**

circuit used in converters to regulate output voltage. Regulation is achived by varying the conduction time of the transistor switches.

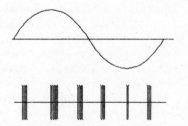

■ **purchased power**

power purchased from other utilities.

■ **pure inductors**

used at all frequencies to provide an electronic circuit with inductive reactance.

■ **push-pull**

a switching power supply topology where power is delivered to the load during the whole input cycle. These can achieve power levels in excess of 1000VA. Push-pull transformers are practical at low input voltages and higher output power. They are not advisable for off line converters because the power switches operate at collector stress voltages of twice the supply voltage.

■ **push-pull converter**

converter topology usually configured as a forward converter, but uses two transistor switches and a centre tapped transformer. The transistor switches turn on and off alternately. Also see **boost regulator, buck regulator, bridge converter, flyback converter** and **resonant converter.**

■ **PX**

the Power Exchange. The wholesale electricity market in California where electricity is bought and sold much like a stock exchange.

■ **Q**

the Q value of an inductor is a measure of the relative losses in a inductor. The Q is also known as the quality factor and is technically defined as the ratio of inductive reactance to effective resistance and is represented by:Q

■ QA

Quality Assurance.

■ QAM

Quadrature Amplitude Modulation. A two-dimensional modulation used for ADSL, cable modems and proposed for VDSL. CAP is a special case of QAM. In QAM, a single carrier frequency is modulated in both sine and cosine components.

■ quad

a quadrillion BTUs (1015 BTUs). This is an enormous number equivalent to 3.6 x 106 metric tons of coal, or 172,000,000 (1.72 x 106) barrels of oil. A quadrillion is the number one followed by 15 zeros. It would be impossible to count to such a number even if you counted by 1,000s for every second of your life until you were 100 years old. The United States used about 80 quads of energy in 1990.

■ quadratic form

any function of the form $f(x) = x^H Q x$, where Q is a square matrix and x is a vector of suitable dimension. Here x^H denotes the conjugate transpose of the vector x.

■ quartz

the crystalline form of Silicon Dioxide (SiO_2). Quartz is the material from which a blank is made.

■ quartz crystal unit

a completed quartz crystal, consisting of a resonator plate with electrodes, a holder with suitable mounting structures, and a permanently sealed cover. Usually called a 'crystal.'

■ quasi regulated output

the regulation of an auxiliary output that is accomplished by regulation of the main output. A transformer turns ratio, commensurate with the desired auxiliary output voltage, is used in conjunction with the output around which the main control loop is closed. Quasi regulated outputs can be reasonably well regulated, but are significantly affected by second order effects in the converter.

■ R.P.M. (Revolutions Per Minute)

the number of times per minute the shaft of the motor (machine) rotates. This is a function of design and the power supply.

■ r1max

the maximum resistance of a polyswitch device at room temperature one hour after being tripped or after reflow soldering. Synonyms: Maximum Resistance

■ ra max

maximum functional resistance of device before and after defined stress tests.

■ ra min

minimum functional resistance of device before and after defined stress tests.

■ rack

a metal bracket with porcelain

spools to support low-voltage conductors and service wires.

■ **radian**

standard unit of angle: the angle at which the arc of circle has the same length as the radius.

■ **radiation**

See **infrared**

■ **radio frequency interference**

an audible buzz or noise in some sensitive audio and radio equipment caused by the dimmer's rapid current switching in conjunction with sharp current rise.

■ **RADSL**

Rate-Adaptive Digital Subscriber Line. A simple extension of ADSL to encompass a wide variety of data rates depending on the line's transmission capability. RADSL can either CAP or DMT ADSL.

■ **rainproof**

so constructed, projected, or treated as to prevent rain from interfering with the successful operation of the apparatus under specified test conditions.

■ **raintight**

so constructed or protected that exposure to a beating rain will not result in the entrance of water.

■ **raise/lower controls**

an actuator (slider, rocker, toggle, paddle, etc.) which when engaged increases or decreases the intensity of light controlled, then returns to its normal place of rest after disengaging.

■ **ramp voltage**

a steadily rising voltage.

■ **Random Access Memory (RAM)**

memory that can be both read and changed during computer operation. Unlike other semi-conductor memories, RAM is volatile-if power to the RAM is disrupted or lost, all the data stored is lost.

■ **random wound**

the standard type of stator winding used in motors under 1,000 volts. The coils are random wound with round wire as opposed to flat form wound coils.

■ **range**

Those values over which a transducer is intended to measure, specified by its upper and lower limits.

■ **rangeability**

the ratio of the maximum flowrate to the minimum flowrate of a meter.

■ **rankine (°r)**

an absolute temperature scale based upon the Fahrenheit scale with 180° between the ice point and boiling point of water. $459.67°R = 0°F.$

■ **RAP**

Reconnect service At the Pole.

■ **rate action**

The derivative function of a temperature controller.

■ **rate schedules**

reflect the amount SCE charges

for various services, when becoming a customer of the Company. (Provide link to Tariff Book).

■ **rate time**

the time interval over which the system temperature is sampled for the derivative function.

■ **rated current**

the level of continuous DC current that can be passed through the inductor. This DC current level is based on a maximum temperature rise of the inductor at the maximum rated ambient temperature. The rated current is related to the inductor's ability to minimise the power losses in the winding by having a low DC resistance. It is also related to the inductor's ability to dissipate this power loss in the windings. Thus, the rated current can be increased by reducing the DC resistance or increasing the inductor size.For low frequency current waveforms the RMS current can be substituted for the DC rated current. The rated current is not related to the magnetic properties of the inductor (Also see Incremental Current and Saturation Current)

■ **rated output current**

The maximum load current that a power supply can provide at a specified ambient temperature.

■ **ratiometric measurement**

a measurement technique where an external signal is used to provide the voltage reference for the dual-slope A/D converter. The external signal can be derived from

the voltage excitation applied to a bridge circuit or pick-off supply, thereby eliminating errors due to power supply fluctuations.

■ **raw material**

the original material as taken from its source, usually the ground. A good example is bauxite ore that is used to make aluminum.

■ **RCAP**

Reconnect Cut At Pole.

■ **reactance**

the opposition to an alternating current presented by inductance, capacitance, or a combination of the two. Reactance is measured in 'ohms' and is represented by the letter 'X.'

■ **reactance (inductive)**

the characteristic of a coil, when connected to alternating current, which causes the current to lag the voltage in time phase. The current wave reaches its peak later than the voltage wave reaches its peak.

■ **Read Only Memory (ROM)**

Memory that contains fixed data. The computer can read the data, but cannot change it in any way.

■ **real time**

the time interval over which the system temperature is sampled for the derivative function.

■ **receiver**

appointed by the court, in a bankruptcy case, to manage that affairs of an enterprise in reOrganisation or liquidation.

■ recloser

device that is initiated when a power circuit breaker is opened and will close the breaker for a test after a pre-set length of time.

■ recombination

the action by which current carriers (electrons and holes) combine and cancel each other.

■ record

a collection of unrelated information that is treated as a single unit.

■ recovery time

the length of time, which it takes a transducer to return to normal after applying a proof pressure.

■ rectification

the process of using a diode to convert and AC voltage into DC. There are two general types of retificitaion processes, half-wave and full-wave.

■ rectifier

device that allows current to flow in only one direction, such as a diode.

■ recycle

to recycle is to put into the cycle again. In other words, to take a product and reuse it when discarded. Recycling saves enormous amounts of energy and raw materials.

■ redox potential

the potential developed by a metallic electrode when placed in a solution containing a species in two different oxidation states.

■ redundancy

utilising multiple access methods so that if one goes down the systems still operate.

■ redundant power supply

a second power supply circuit sometimes specified for systems used in critical applications. Redundancy is useful where unexpected power failures can cause a major system to fail, often at great expense. Redundant power supplies could be fed from different AC power (mains) circuits for maximum system reliability. Power supplies are usually 'diode orded' and should be hot swappable. A 'redundant capacity' supply is usually a single supply with built-in r arallel configuration of converters used in distributed power system to increase system reliability. Converters may be used in a 'N+1' architecture.

■ reed relay

consists of two thin magnetic strips (reeds). When a coil close to the reeds is energised, they are magnetised and drawn together making a connection between leads attached to the reeds.

■ reference command

refers to an externally applied signal which represents a command; usually represents the desired output.

■ reference junction

the cold junction in a thermocouple circuit which is held at a stable known temperature. The standard reference temperature is

0°C (32°F). However, other temperatures can be used.

■ reference mark

random graduation pattern which - when traversed over - produces a signal peak, which may be used to determine an absolute datum within an incremental measuring system.

■ reference plane

any plane perpendicular to the shaft axis to which an amount of unbalance is referred.

■ reference pulse

square-wave signal produced when the scale reference mark is traversed over; normally one measuring step wide; may be used to define an absolute datum within an incremental measuring system.

■ reflected ripple current

the RMS or peak-to-peak AC current present at the input of the power supply which is a result of the switching frequency of the converter.

■ refractory metal thermocouple

a class of thermocouples with melting points above 3600°F. The most common are made from tungsten and tungsten/rhenium alloys Types G and C. They can be used for measuring high temperatures up to 4000°F (2200°C) in non-oxidising, inert, or vacuum environments.

■ refresh rate

also referred to as scan rate. It is the number of times in one second (Measured in Hz) that the electron beam travels across the screen horizontally from one scan line to the next.

■ region of convergence (roc)

the region of convergence of a transform F(s) refers to those values s in the complex plane for which the Laplace Transform integral yields a finite number; i.e. is well defined. See **laplace transform**.

■ register

a storage device with a specific capacity, such as a bit, byte or word.

■ regulation

ability of a converter to maintain an output voltage to within specified limits under varying conditions of input line and output load. Also see **linear regulation**.

■ regulation band

the total error band allowable for an output voltage. This includes the effects of all of the types of regulation: line, load, and cross.

■ regulator

a device for controlling the voltage of an electrical circuit.

■ relay

an electrically controlled mechanical device that opens and closes electrical contacts when a voltage (or current) is applied to a coil. A relay provides isolation of control signals from switched signals.

■ **relay (mechanical)**

An electromechanical device that completes or interrupts a circuit by physically moving electrical contacts into contact with each other.

■ **relayed**

the power circuit breaker has opened.

■ **reliability**

the ability to deliver uninterrupted electricity to consumers on demand, and to withstand sudden disturbances such as short circuits or loss of major system components. This encompasses both the reliability of the generation system and of the transmission and distribution system. Reliability may be evaluated by the frequency, duration and magnitude of any adverse effects on consumer service.

■ **reluctance**

the opposition of a material to magnetic lines of force. Reluctance in the magnetic circuit corresponds to resistance in the electric circuit.

■ **reluctance synchronous motor**

a synchronous motor with a special rotor design which directly lines the rotor up with the rotating magnetic field of the stator, allowing for no slip under load. The reluctance motors have lower efficiencies, power factors and torques than their permanent magnet counterparts.

■ **remote**

not hard-wired; communicating via switched lines, such as telephone lines. Usually refers to peripheral devices that are located a site away from the CPU.

■ **remote inhibit**

a power supply interface signal, usually TTL compatible, which commands the power supply to shut down one or all outputs.

■ **remote lan access**

a data communications such as a corporate or campus environment in which the computer networks can be accessed remotely via public telecommunications networks.

■ **remote meter dial**

additional meter dial supplied by Edison customer when access problem exists.

■ **remote sensing**

using sense leads connected at the output load provides feedback to voltage regulation circuits of a converter. This arrangement is used to compensate for voltage losses from long leads to a load. Also see **local sensing**.

■ **remote shutdown**

see **logic inhibit/enable**.

■ **repeatability**

the ability of a transducer to reproduce output readings when the same measurand value is applied to it consecutively, under the same conditions, and in the same direction. Repeatability is expressed as the maximum difference between output readings.

■ **repeater**

an electronic device used to regenerate digital signals and restore signal and restore signal quality across a certain distance of cable.

■ **reserved word**

a word that has a defined function in the language, and cannot be used as a variable name.

■ **residual (final) unbalance**

residual unbalance is that unbalance of any kind that remains after balancing.

■ **residual flux**

the flux that remains in a core when the applied MMF is returned to zero.

■ **resilient mounting**

a suspension system or cushioned mounting designed to reduce the transmission of normal motor noise and vibration to the mounting surface. This type of mounting is typically used in fractional motors for fans and blowers.

■ **resistance**

in physics, that property of a substance that restricts the flow or electricity through it, associated with the conversion of electrical energy to heat; also the magnitude of this property. Resistance depends on many factors, such as the nature of the material, its temperature, dimensions, and thermal properties; degree of impurity; the nature and state of illumination of the surface; and the frequency and

magnitude of the current. The SI unit of resistance is the ohm.

■ **resistance binned devices**

resistance binned devices are supplied such that all parts in one package are within 0.5 ? of each other. Individual binned packages are supplied from the full resistance limits of the specified product.

■ **resistance ratio characteristic**

for thermistors, the ratio of the resistance of the thermistor at 25°C to the resistance at 125°C.

■ **resistance sorted devices**

resistance sorted devices (part number suffix Rx) are supplied with resistance values that are within specified limits of the products full range of resistance.

■ **resistance temperature characteristic**

A relationship between a thermistor's resistance and the temperature.

■ **Resistance Temperature Device (RTD)**

Resistance Temperature Devices (or detectors) rely on the principle that the resistance of a metal increases with temperature. When made of platinum, they may be known as platinum resistance thermometers (PRTs).

■ **resistance weld**

Procedure involving pressure sealing with electricity and backfilling with nitrogen to force out oxygen and moisture. This results in superior aging characteristics.

resistance, maximum

the maximum resistance of a polyswitch device at room temperature one hour after being tripped or after reflow soldering. Synonyms: R1max

resistance, post-reflow

the resistance of a polyswitch device at room temperature one hour after it has been connected to a circuit board by reflow soldering under specified conditions.

resistance, post-trip

the resistance of a polyswitch device at room temperature one hour after the device has been tripped for the first time, under specified conditions.

resistor

a component used to introduce resistance into a circuit.

resolution

the smallest detectable increment of measurement. Resolution is usually limited by the number of bits used to quantize the input signal. For example, a 12-bit A/D can resolve to one part in 4096 (2 to the 12 power equals 4096).

resolver

inductive angle measuring device, producing two alternating voltages whose amplitudes or phases depend on the (shaft) rotation angle.

resonance

the creation of vibrations in a system by the application of a periodic force. The state which exists when the frequency of the applied force is equal to the natural frequency of the system.

resonant converter

switching converter technology in which a resonant tank circuit operating at very high frequencies is used to transfer energy to the output.

resonant frequency

the natural frequency at which a circuit oscillates or a device vibrates. Abbreviated as "Fr" or "fr."

resonator

a body that is capable of being set into resonance by the application of a periodic force.

resource

from the Latin word "resurgere" meaning "to rise again." A substance for which there is an identifiable use within society. Prior to 1939, uranium was not a resource until it was developed for use in nuclear power, medicine and weapons production.

response time (time constant)

the time required by a sensor to reach 63.2% of a step change in temperature under a specified set of conditions. Five time constants are required for the sensor to stabilise at 600 of the step change value.

retail consumers

consumers, including residences and businesses, who themselves use the electricity that they purchase; also referred to as end-use consumers.

■ retail wheeling

a transmission or distribution service by which utilities deliver electric power sold by a third party directly to retail consumers. This would allow an individual retail consumer to choose his or her electricity supplier, but still receive delivery using the power lines of the local utility.

■ return

common terminal on the output of a DC-DC converter. It is the return current path for the output. Also see Common.

■ return loss

the ratio of the power launched into a cable and the power of the light returned down the fiber. This measurement is expressed in positive decibel units (db). A higher number is better. Return Loss = 10 log (incident power/returned power).

■ revenue

a rate component that reflects customer charge, when applicable, and the basic rate. The yield from our investment.

■ reversal error

measuring error which results from approaching a position from different directions.

■ reverse bias

a dc voltage applied to a PN junction so that the positive terminal of the voltage source connects to the N-type material and the nega-

tive terminal to the P-type material. It produces reverse current in the circuit.

■ reverse current

current in a circuit of a semiconductor device due to conduction by minority carriers across PN junction.

■ reverse voltage protection

converter feature that prevents damage to internal components if a reverse voltage is inadvertently applied to the input or output terminals.

■ reversible temperature coefficient

changes in flux which occurs with temperature change. They are spontaneously regained when the temperature is returned to its original point. There are two values reported: reversible temperature coefficients of inductance (Br) and Coercivity (Hci). The temperature range over which they have been measured and specified should be stated. Most materials exhibit a non-linear response with temperature.

■ reversing

unless otherwise specified, a general-purpose DC motor is reversible. A DC motor can be reversed by changing the polarity of the field or the armature, but not both. When rapid reversing is necessary, the armature circuit is reversed. In some cases, it is frequently more advantageous to reverse the field connections of shunt motors, since the controls have to handle much less current, especially on large motors, than do armature-circuit contactors. An AC motor is reversed by reversing the connections of one leg on three-phase power or by reversing the leads on single phase.

reynolds number

the ratio of inertial and viscous forces in a fluid defined by the formula $Re = rVD/\mu$, where: $r =$ Density of fluid, $\mu =$ Viscosity in centipoise (CP), $V =$ Velocity, and $D =$ Inside diameter of pipe.

RF

Radio Frequency

RFI

an abbreviation for Radio Frequency Interference, which is undesirable noise produced by a power supply or other electrical or electronic device during its operation. In power supply technology, RFI is usually taken to mean the same thing as EMI.

RFP

Request For Proposal

RGB

a three-component video signal in which all the colours in a scene or image are conveyed as three primary colours (Red, Green and Blue) on three separate channels. Some times, the Green signal also carries the Sync information as well. Many high resolution video monitors have RGB inputs.

rheostat

a variable resistor.

rigid rotor

a rotor is considered rigid when it can be corrected in any two (arbitrarily selected) planes [see **correction (balancing) plane**] and after that correction, its unbalance does not significantly exceed the balancing tolerances (relative to the shaft axis) at any speed up to maximum operating speed and when running under conditions which approximate closely to those of the final supporting system.

ring

a network topology where nodes are connected in a ring. Used in Token Ring and SONET networks.

ripple

the difference between maximum and minimum attenuation in the passband.

ripple and noise

The amplitude of the AC component on the DC output of a power supply usually expressed in millivolts peak-to-peak or RMS. For a linear power supply it is usually the frequency of the AC mains. For a switching power supply, it is usually the switching frequency of the converter stage.

ripple voltage

the periodic alternating voltage imposed on the voltage output of a switching voltage converter. The ripple voltage is normally specified as a peak-to-peak value.

rise time

refers to the time required for the

output of a system to reach 90% of the final output value in response to a specific input. The rise time depends on the applied signal and on the dynamical properties of the system (e.g. time constants).

■ **risers**

wires or cables that are run vertically from one floor of a building to another to supply electric current.

■ **Rmax**

the resistance of a polyswitch device under specified conditions (e.g., 20 °C), before connection into a circuit. Devices of a particular type will be delivered with a range of resistances; therefore, a minimum value, Rmin, and/or a maximum value, Rmax, are often given. Synonyms: Initial Resistance, Base Resistance, Rmin, or Resistance

■ **Rmin**

the resistance of a polyswitch device under specified conditions (e.g., 20 °C), before connection into a circuit. Devices of a particular type will be delivered with a range of resistances; therefore, a minimum value, Rmin, and/or a maximum value, Rmax, are often given. Synonyms: Initial Resistance, Base Resistance,Resistance,or Rmax

■ **RMS**

Root Mean Square. The square root of the sum of the squares

of a set of quantities divided by the total number of quantities. Used when monitoring ac (alternating current) signals. Many power supplies, for example, issue an ac signal. This needs to be converted to a dc (direct current) signal for the PC interface. The solution is a signal conditioning input that produces a dc signal proportional to the rms of the amplitude of the input signal. The rms operation means the reading will always be positive.

■ **roller bearing**

a special bearing system with cylindrical rollers capable of handling belted applications, too large for standard ball bearings.

■ **room conditions**

ambient environmental conditions under which transducers must commonly operate.

■ **root mean square (rms)**

square root of the mean of the square of the signal taken during one full cycle.

■ **Root Mean Square (RMS) value**

see **effective value**.

■ **rotating magnetic field**

the force created by the stator once power is applied to it that causes the rotor to turn.

■ **rotor**

the rotating member of an induction motor made up of stacked laminations. A shaft running

through the centre and a squirrel cage made in most cases of aluminium which holds the laminations together and act as a conductor for the induced magnetic field. The squirrel cage is made by casting molten aluminium into the slots cut into each lamination.

■ **rough service lamp**

a lamp with extra filament support which can help reduce lamp buzz.

■ **router**

a network device that interconnects networks. Routers provide traffic control and filtering functions, they are commonly used to connect a LAN to the Internet.

■ **routh table**

a table formed from the coefficients of a polynomial. The table is used to determine the number of right half plane roots of the polynomial. It is also useful for determining the location of any roots which are symmetric with respect to the origin.

■ **routine**

a routine test is a basic test done in the factory to the requirements of

NEMA MG1, paragraph 12.51 and IEEE-112-1978 and includes the following measurements: no load current/watts; winding resistance; and high potential test.

■ **royer converter**

self-oscillating, push-pull switching circuit configuration commonly used in low cost, low power DC-DC converters. Also called the classical converter.

■ **rs-232**

an asynchronous serial data interchange standard. RS-232 links between equipment are normally limited to 50 feet (16 meters). Also referred to as RS-232C (most popular revision).

■ **rs-422**

a more robust serial digital data interchange standard utilising individual differential signal pairs for data transmission in each direction. Depending on data transmission rates, RS-422 can be used at distances to 4,000 feet (1,275 meters). Also referred to as RS-422A (the most popular revision).

■ **rs485**

another EIA protocol for serial communications. Allows several devices to be connected to a single cable, distributed over a wide area.

■ **rs-485**

a very robust serial data interchange standard. An RS-485 communications channel is a party-line (multi-drop) digital signal and, like RS-422, is balanced. It is very immune to interference, making it more reliable in demanding environments. It is usable at distances of 4,000 feet and beyond.

rtd (resistance thermal detectors)

a resistance device used to measure temperature change in the motor windings to detect a possible over heating condition. These detectors would be embedded into the winding slot and their resistance varies with the temperature.

rural electric cooperative

(Cooperatively owned electric utility) a consumer-owned electric utility that was created to transmit and distribute power in rural areas. Rural electric cooperatives benefit from below-market financing from the Rural Utilities Service (formerly the Rural Electrification Administration), as well as low-cost power from federal hydroelectric projects. In addition, most do not pay state or federal income taxes. Rates for rural electric cooperatives typically are set by a board of directors elected from among the cooperative's members. Today, rural electric cooperatives serve about 11 percent of the nation's electric consumers.

safety ground

a conductive path to earth that is designed to protect persons from electrical shock by shunting away any dangerous currents that might occur due to malfunction or accident.

salt bridge

the salt bridge of a reference electrode is that part of the electrode which contains the filling solution to establish the electrolytic connection between reference internal cell and the test solution. Auxiliary Salt Bridge: A glass tube open at one end to receive intermediate electrolyte filling solution, and the reference electrode tip and a junction at the other end to make contact with the sample.

salt effect (fx)

The effect on the activity coefficient due to salts in the solution.

SAMA

Scientific Apparatus Makers Association. An association that has issued standards covering platinum, nickel, and copper resistance elements (RTDs).

sample and hold

a component of a type of analogue-to-digital converter. The analogue signal is frozen in a sample and hold circuit to prevent it changing during digitisation.

saturable reactor

describes the main element of a magnetic amplifier used to control electrical power such as for electrical resistance element heating of furnaces.

saturation

exists when an increase in magnetising force (H) does not cause a corresponding increase in the flux density (B) of the material. The cause of saturation is relative to the magnetic properties of the core. Each material can store only a given amount of magnetic flux density. Beyond this the permeability of the core is reduced dramatically causing inductance to fall.

■ saturation current

the DC bias current flowing through tile inductor which causes the inductance to drop by a specified amount form the initial zero DC bias inductance value. Common specified inductance drop percentages include 1-% and 20%. IT is useful to use the 10% inductance drop value for ferrite cores and 20% for powdered iron cores in energy storage applications.The cause of the inductance to drop due to the DC bias current is related to the magnetic properties of the core. The core, and some of the space around the core, can only store a given amount of magnetic ~ density. Beyond the maximum flux density point, the permeabilty of the core is reduced. Thus, the inductance is caused to drop. Core saturation does not apply to air-core inductors (Also see incremental current and permeability)

■ saturation flux density

the flux density value at which a given material saturates.

■ scada

supervisory control and data acquisition - a large scale software package usually used to monitor and control a manufacturing process.

■ scan

normal channel scanning in a data acquisition system involves

stepping round and reading each input channel in turn. The scan will return to the first channel once all the channels have been sampled.

■ scanning frequency

response level which limits the velocity of an incremental measuring system.

■ scattering (fiber optic)

scattering occurs when light collides with individual atoms in the glass. This is one of several causes of attenuation.

■ sce

Saturated Calomel Electrode.

■ scene

the lighting effect created by adjusting several zones/channels of lighting to the desired intensity.

■ SCR

Silicone Controlled Rectifier.

■ screens

are protection which can be placed over openings in the fan cover on a fan-cooled motor or ventilation openings of a protected motor to help keep out large particles and/or animals, but not block ventilation.

■ scroll

to move all or part of the screen material up or down, left or right, to allow new information to appear.

■ SDH

Synchronous Digital Hierarchy

■ SDSL

Symmetric Digital Subscriber Line.

■ second

the basic unit of measure of time, equivalent to 'the duration of 9,192,631,770 periods of the radiation corresponding to the transition between the two hyperfine levels of the ground state of the cesium-133 atom.' For our purposes, one 'second' is 1/60th of a minute.

■ second law of thermodynamics

the Second Law of Thermodynamics states that the universe constantly tends toward a state of maximum disorder, or entropy. No process involving energy transformation will spontaneously occur unless energy is degraded from an orderly, concentrated form into a disorderly, dispersed form.

■ secondaries

output side of transformer. Low-voltage lines, 120/240 volt for residential, 120/240, 120/208, 244/480, and 277/408 volt for commercial, that carry power from the transformer to the poles nearby.

■ secondary circuit

output side of an isolated DC-DC converter. Also see **primary circuit**.

■ secondary device

a part of the flowmeter which receives a signal proportional to the flowrate, from the primary device, and displays, records and/or transmits the signal.

■ secondary standard

pH buffer solutions which do not meet the requirements of primary standard solutions but provide coverage of the pH range not covered by primary standards. Used when the pH value of the primary standard is not close to the sample pH value.

■ secondary winding

the winding in a transformer that supplies the load with electrical energy which has been converted from the induced magnetic energy in the core.

■ seebeck coefficient

the derivative (rate of change) of thermal EMF with respect to temperature normally expressed as millivolts per degree.

■ seebeck effect

the principle that describes how a thermocouple works. In a circuit in which there are junctions between dissimilar metals, an electromotive force (voltage) is set up when the junctions are at different temperatures.

■ seebeck emf

The open circuit voltage caused by the difference in temperature between the hot and cold junctions of a circuit made from two dissimilar metals.

■ self heating

internal heating of a transducer as a result of power dissipation.

■ self resonant frequency

the frequency at which an inductorOs distributed capacitance resonates with the inductance. The inductive reactance and the capacitive reactance are equal. The inductor acts as a pure resistance. The Q of an inductor is equal to zero at the SRF.

■ self-calibrating

a data acquisition card or module with a stable on-board reference voltage that software can use for automatic recalibration.

■ self-contained metering

indicates that all the current that is used by the customer, will pass through the meter.

■ self-inductance

the ability of a circuit or coil to induce a voltage within itself.

■ self-induction

the process by which a changing current induces a voltage into the conductor or coil carrying the current.

■ self-powered hub

class of devices that derive power from its own source. Examples include monitors and self-powered USB hubs.

■ self-terminating

a switching configuration which automatically terminates a signal path when it is not connected to any other signal path. It is usually most important to terminate unused inputs to a unit to assist in reducing noise and improve crosstalk isolation.

■ SELV

an abbreviation for Safety Extra Low Voltage, a term generally defined by the regulatory agencies as the highest voltage that can be contacted by a person and not cause injury. It is often specifically defined as 30 VAC or 42.4 VDC.

■ sendust

a 9% silicon, 6% aluminum, and 85% iron alloy in particulate form. The particles are coated with a dielectric film, compacted, and cured to form magnetic parts such as inductor cores.

■ sense line

output line used in a remote sensing connection to route the output voltage (at the load) back to the control feedback loop. Also see **remote sensing.**

■ sensing element

that part of the transducer which reacts directly in response to the input.

■ sensitivity

the minimum change in input signal to which an instrument can respond.

■ sensitivity shift

a change in slope of the calibration curve due to a change in sensitivity.

■ sensitivity transfer function

given a negative feedback system with open loop transfer function L, the sensitivity transfer function denoted S is defined as follows: $S(s) = 1/(1 + L(s))$.

■ **sensor**

a device that can detect a change in a physical quantity (light or pressure for example) and produce a corresponding electrical signal.

■ **separately derived system**

a premises wiring system whose power is derived from a battery, a solar photovoltaic system, or from a generator, transformer, or converter windings, and that has no direct electrical connection, including solidly connected grounded circuit conductor, to supply conductors originating in another system.

■ **sequencing**

the mode during which preset lighting scenes change in a designated order using fade times that have been programmed.

■ **sequential access**

an access mode in which records are retrieved in the same order in which they were written. Each successive access to the file refers to the next record in the file.

■ **serial communication**

where data is transferred one bit at a time.

■ **serial transmission**

sending one bit at a time on a single transmission line. Compare with parallel transmission.

■ **series compensation**

refers to a compensator which is in series with the plant. Other forms of compensation include Parallel Compensations and Feedforward Compensation.

■ **series dc motors**

where high starting torques are required for a DC motor, the series motor is used. The load must be solidly connected to the motor and never decrease to zero to prevent excessive motor speeds. The load must tolerate wide speed variations from full load to light load. Typical areas of application are industrial trucks, hoists, cranes, and traction duty.

■ **series operation**

master-slave configuration in which two or more isolated converters are connected to obtain a hgher output voltage level (converter inputs connected in parallel) or wider input voltage range (converter inputs connected in series) than that obtainable from one module. Also see **master-slave operation**.

■ **series regulator**

linear regulator (internal or external to the converter)placed in a series with the load to achieve a constant voltage across the load. This is the most popular method of linear regulation. Also see **linear regulation, post regulation** and **shunt regulator**.

■ **series resonance**

the condition that exists when a crystal unit is operated without the presence of load capacitance. 'Series Resonance' is frequently shortened to the word 'series.' See **'Load Resonance.'**

■ **server**

a computing device that provides

a service to users on a network (clients). An example is a file server that stores and maintains documents for retrieval.

■ **service conductors**

the supply conductors that extend from the street main or transformers to the service equipment of the premises being supplied

■ **service drop**

run of cables from the power company's aerial power lines to the point of connection to a customer's premises.

■ **service entrance**

the point where the service wires enter a building.

■ **service entrance conductors**

(Overhead) the service conductors between the terminals of the service equipment and a point usually outside the building, clear of building walls, where joined by tap or splice to the service drop.

■ **service equipment**

the necessary equipment, usually consisting of a circuit breaker or switch and fuses and their accessories, located near the point entrance of supply conductors to a building and intended to constitute the main control and cutoff means for the supply to the building.

■ **service factor**

1. when used on a motor nameplate, a number which indicates how much above the nameplate rating a motor can be loaded without causing serious degradation,

(i.e., a 1.15 S-F can produce 15% greater torque than the 1.0 S-F rating of the same motor). 2. When used in applying motors or gearmotors, a figure of merit which is used to "adjust" measured loads in an attempt to compensate for conditions which are difficult to measure or define. Typically, measured loads are multiplied by service factors (experience factors) and the result in an "equivalent required torque" rating of a motor or gearmotor.

■ **service lateral**

the underground service conductors between the street main, including any risers at a pole or other structure or from transformers, and the first point of connection to the service-entrance conductors in a terminal box, meter, or other enclosure with adequate space, inside or outside the building wall. Where there is no terminal box, meter, or other enclosure with adequate space, the point of connection is the entrance point of the service conductors into the building.

■ **service limiter**

limits electricity use to 120 volts and 5 or 10 amps = approx. 600-1,200 volts.

■ **service lines**

also known as DROPS. Lines that carry power from secondary lines at pole to each individual customer.

■ **service obligation**

a term used to mean the duties a regulated public utility must perform for its consumers. Service obligation includes the duty: 1) to serve all prospective consumers; 2) to provide adequate, reliable service; and 3) to render safe, efficient and nondiscriminatory service.

■ **service point**

the point of connection between the facilities of the serving utility and the premises wiring.

■ **service switch**

the main switch which connects all load in a building to the service wires.

■ **service wires**

also known as DROPS. Lines that carry power from secondary lines at a pole to each individual customer.

■ **set point**

the temperature at which a controller is set to control a system.

■ **set up transformer**

when the secondary is at a higher voltage than

■ **settle time**

the time required for establishing relay connections and stabilising user circuits. For relay contacts, this includes contact bounce.

■ **shaft**

the rotating member of the motor which protrudes past the bearings for attachment to the driven apparatus.

■ **s-hdsl**

single pair transmission using HDSL technology, normally 2B1Q.

■ **shear modulus**

the ratio of the shear stress and the angular shear distortion.

■ **shear stress**

where normal stress is perpendicular to the designated plane, shear stress is parallel to the plane.

■ **shearing strain**

a measure of angular distortion also directly measurable, but not as easily as axial strain.

■ **sheath thermocouple**

a thermocouple made out of mineral-insulated thermocouple cable which has an outer metal sheath.

■ **shielded inductor**

an inductor designed for its core to contain a majority of its magnetic field. Some inductor designs are self shielding. Examples of these are magnetic core shapes which include toroids, pot cores and B-Cores. Magnetic core shapes such as slug cores and bobbins require the application of a magnetic sleeve or similar method to yield a shielded inductor. It should be noted that magnetic shielding is a matter of degree. A certian percentage of the magnetic field will escape the core material. This is even applicable to toroidal cores as lower core permeabilities will have higher fringing field than will high permeability toroidal cores (Also see **closed magnetic path**.)

■ **shielding**

a conductive foil or braid that covers insulated wires in a cable. The shield provides electrical grounding and protection from external electromagnetic interference (EMI). Shielding is also used to control internal electromagnetic radiation.

■ **shock**

the sensory impression caused by an electrical current flow through the body.

■ **short**

an accidental connection of low resistance, such as in an electrical cord with wires exposed contacting each other.

■ **short circuit protection**

see **current limit** and **foldback current limit**.

■ **short-circuit**

a defect in a winding which causes part of the normal electrical circuit to be bypassed. This frequently results in reducing the resistance or impedance to such an extent as to cause overheating of the winding, and subsequent burnout.

■ **shunt capacitance**

a parameter associated with a quartz crystal unit, used to identify the capacitance resulting from the presence of the electrodes plus stray capacitance associated with the holder.

■ **shunt regulator**

linear regulator (internal or external to the converter) placed in parallel with the load to achieve a constant voltage across the load. Also see **Linear Regulation, Post**

Regulation and **Series Regulator.**

■ **shunt wound dc motors**

integral-horsepower shunt motors, are used where the primary load requirements are for minimum speed variation from full-load to no-load and/or constant horsepower over an adjustable speed range at constant potential. Shunt motors are suitable for average starting torque loads. Typical applications include individual drives for machine tools, such as drills and lathes, and centrifugal fans and blowers which are regulated by means of the discharge opening.

■ **SI**

System Internationale. The name given to the standard metric system of units.

■ **side section (fin)**

a scored section along each side of the mounting plate designed to be removed to facilitate ganging.

■ **signal**

an electrical transmittance (either input or output) that conveys information.

■ **signal conditioner**

a circuit module which offsets, attenuates, amplifies, linearizes and/ or filters the signal for input to the A/D converter. The typical output signal conditioner is +2 V dc.

■ **signal conditioning**

to process the form or mode of a signal so as to make it intelligible to, or compatible with, a given device, including such manipulation as pulse shaping, pulse clipping, compensating, digitizing, and linearizing.

■ simple network management protocol

a network management standard initially established to allow multi-vendor networking devices to be managed more easily with common management tools.

■ simple winding

a winding for a toroidal core which results in 78% of the cores inside diameter remaining. Often times this will produce a single layer winding.

■ simultaneous sampling

when all analogue signals are read simultaneously. This is achieved by providing each input with its own A-D converter, and initiating sampling from a single clock. It ensures that there is no reduction in sampling rate when more signals are connected.

■ sine wave

a periodic wave that can be represented by a sine curve. The amplitude of such a wave is a function of the sine of a linear quantity such as phase or time.

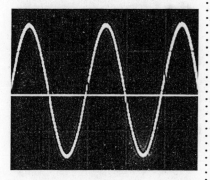

■ single layer winding

a winding for a toroidal core which will result in the full utilisation of the inside circumference of the core without overlapping of turns. The thickness of the wire and tightness of the winding will affect results.

■ single pole

a single pole dimmer provides full-range dimming from one location only.

■ single precision

The degree of numeric accuracy that requires the use of one computer word. In single precision, seven digits are stored, and up to seven digits are printed. Contrast with double precision.

■ single-ended input

a signal-input circuit where SIG LO (or sometimes SIG HI) is tied to METER GND. Ground loops are normally not a problem in AC-powered meters, since METER GND is transformer-isolated from AC GND.

■ single-ended output

a circuit whose output is developed between one output terminal and ground.

■ singlemode

a type of fiber with a small core that allows only one mode of light to propagate.

■ single-phase

a generator or circuit in which only one alternating current voltage is produced. A single-phase circuit will have two or three wires carrying the current.

■ **single-phase motor**

an alternating current motor designed to operate from a single-phase circuit.

■ **single-plane (static) balancing machine**

a single plane balancing machine is a gravitational or centrifugal balancing machine that provides information for accomplishing single plane balancing.

■ **sintered iron**

powdered iron that has been pressed and sintered into a structural form. This type of material occasionally is used in a magnetic application, but they normally exhibit excessive core losses.

■ **sinusoidal**

the graphical plot of the output of an alternator.

■ **SISO**

Single-Input Single-Output.

■ **six-sided shielding**

converter packaging technique in which the unit is placed into a metal case. This metal shielding minimised any noise radiation from the converter components. A continuous shielded case has the base (or header) welded on, further reducing potential noise leakage.

■ **skew**

arrangement of laminations on a rotor or armature to provide a slight angular pattern of their slots with respect to the shaft axis. This pattern helps to eliminate low speed cogging effects in an armature and minimize induced vibration in a rotor as well as reduce associated noise. Also can help to increase starting torque.

■ **skewing of the loop**

when an air gap is added to a magnetic path, the hysteresis loop is made to lean over (permeability is reduced). It is said to be skewed or sheared.

■ **skin effect**

the tendency of an alternating current to flow near the surface of a conductor rather than utilising the entire cross-sectional area. The phenomenon causes the resistance of the conductor to increase with an increase in frequency. The magnetic field associated with the current in the conductor causes eddy currents near the centre of the conductor, which opposes the flow of the main current near the centre of the conductor. The main current is forced further to the surface as the frequency is increased.

■ **slave**

a mainframe that is serially connected to a controlling mainframe (master). The slave is controlled from a master.

■ **sleeve bearings**

a type of bearing with no rolling elements, where the motor shaft rides on a film of oil.

■ **sleeves**

also known as boots. Plastic devices which cover the meter

prongs preventing the flow of electricity. Used to turn off socket-type meters.

■ **slew rate**

the maximum rate of change of an output signal.

■ **slide-to-off dimmer**

slide-to-off models have an on/ off switch activated at the bottom of the linear slide travel.

■ **slip**

the difference between the speed of the rotating magnetic field (which is always synchronous) and the rotor in a non-synchronous induction motor is known as slip and is expressed as a percentage of a synchronous speed. Slip generally increases with an increase in torque.

■ **slip rings**

The rotating contacts which are connected to the loops of a generator.

■ **slope (electrode sensitivity, span)**

See **nernst factor**.

■ **slug core**

a core shaped like a rod, with the winding(s) placed around the diameter.

■ **sma**

a small type of threaded coaxial signal connector typically used in higher frequency applications. This connector is typically usable to 26 GHz.

■ **Small Computer System Interface (SCSI)**

A peripheral interface that is used to connect devices to a computer.

■ **smallest bending radius**

the smallest radius that a strain gauge can withstand in one direction, without special treatment, without suffering visible damage.

■ **smb / smc**

types of small coaxial signal connectors typically used in high frequency applications. SMC threads to the mating connector while the SMB "snaps" to the mating connector.

■ **SMD**

the abbreviation for, Surface Mount Device.

■ **soft line**

a condition where there is substantial impedance present in the AC mains feeding input power to a power supply. The input voltage to the power supply drops significantly with increasing load.

■ **soft magnetic material**

a ferromagnetic material that is easily magnetised and demagnetised.

■ **soft start**

a technique for gradually activating a power supply circuit when the power supply is first turned on. This technique is generally used to provide a gradual rise in output voltages and inrush current limiting.

■ **software**

generally, programs loaded into a computer from external mass storage but also extended to include operating systems and documentation.

■ **software trigger**

a programmed event, such as a specific key press or mouse click, that triggers data capture.

■ **soho**

Small Office Home Office

■ **solar energy**

energy derived from the sun's radiation. The amount of energy falling on just 0.3861 sq. mil/1 sq. km is about 4,000 megawatts, enough to heat and light a small town. In one second the Sun gives off 13 million times more energy than all the electricity used in the U.S. in one year. Solar heaters have industrial or domestic uses. They usually consist of a black (heat-absorbing) panel containing pipes through which air or water, heated by the sun, is circulated, either by thermal convection or by a pump. Solar energy may also be harnessed indirectly using solar cells (photovoltaic cells) made of panels of semiconductor material (usually silicon), which generate electricity when illuminated by sunlight. Although it is difficult to generate a high output from solar energy compared to sources such as nuclear or fossil fuels, it is a major nonpolluting and renewable energy source used as far north as Scandinavia as well as in the southwest U.S. and Mediterranean countries.

■ **soldering**

a means of securing an electrical contact to a wire by heating a low alloy of tin and lead also known as solder.

■ **solid state relay**

a relay that switches electric circuits by use of semiconductor elements without moving parts or conventional contacts.

■ **solid waste energy**

the term solid waste energy refers to organic material that can be burned directly or chemically converted to produce heat. In turn, this heat can be used to produce electricity.

■ **solid wire (or conductor)**

one strand of wire. Usually less flexible, lower in cost and lower in resistance than stranded wire of the same AWG. Solid wire is typically used in permanent installations where flexing does not occur.

■ **solvation**

ions in solution are normally combined with at least one molecule of solvent. This phenomenon is termed solvation.

■ **solvent resistance test**

a test described in Raychems PS300 publication to test the durability of the markings on polyswitch devices when exposed to various solvents.

■ **sonet**

synchronous Optical Network- A recently emerging networking standard that utilises fiber optics to create backbone networks, capable of transmitting at extremely high speeds and accommodating gigabit-level bandwidth.

■ sorted

binned refers to resistance-matched devices, which are supplied such that all parts in one particular package (or reel) are within 0.5 ohms of each other (1.0 ohms for TR250-080T devices). Individual matched packages are supplied from the full resistance range of the specified device. The benefit is that resistance-matched devices reduce the tip-ring resistance differential, reducing the possibility of line imbalance. Sorted devices are those that are supplied with resistance values that are within specified segments of the device's full range of resistance, giving greater design flexibility. Synonyms: Binned

■ source

the equipment providing a signal to the input of a routing switcher, crosspoint switch, or switching array.

■ source code

a non-executable program written in a high-level language. A compiler or assembler must translate the source code into object code (machine language) that the computer can understand and process.

■ space charge

in an electron tube, a cloud of free electrons surrounding the emitter.

■ space heater

small resistance heater units mounted in a motor, that are energized, during motor shutdown, to prevent condensation of mois-

ture on the motor windings.

■ span

the difference between the upper and lower limits of a range expressed in the same units as the range.

■ span adjustment

the ability to adjust the gain of a process or strain meter so that a specified display span in engineering units corresponds to a specified signal span. For instance, a display span of 200°F may correspond to the 16 mA span of a 4-20 mA transmitter signal.

■ span guy

a guy wire attached directly from a pole or structure to another pole or structure.

■ spanning tree

an algorithm, the original version of which was invented by Digital Equipment Corporation used to prevent bridging loops by creating a spanning tree. The algorithm is now documented in the IEEE 802.1d specification, although the Digital algorithm and the IEEE 802.1d algorithm are not the same, nor are they compatible.

■ spare

a connector point reserved for options, specials, or other configurations. The point is identified at a location on the electrical schematic.

■ special purpose motor

motor with special operating characteristics or special mechanical construction, or both, designed for a particular application and not falling within the definition of a general purpose or definite purpose motor.

■ **specific gravity**

the ratio of mass of any material to the mass of the same volume of pure water at 4°C.

■ **specific heat**

the ratio of thermal energy required to raise the temperature of a body 1° to the thermal energy required to raise an equal mass of water 1°.

■ **spectral filter**

a filter which allows only a specific band width of the electromagnetic spectrum to pass, i.e., 4 to 8 micron infrared radiation.

■ **spectrum**

the resolving of overall vibration into amplitude components as a function of frequency.

■ **spectrum analysis**

utilising frequency components of a vibration signal to determine the source and cause of vibration.

■ **spike**

short pulse of voltage or current - usually undesirable.

■ **splash-proof motor**

an open motor in which the ventilating openings are so constructed that drops of liquid or solid particles falling on it or coming toward it in a straight line at any angle not greater than 100 degrees from the vertical, cannot enter either directly or by striking and

running along a surface of the motor.

■ **splice**

the joining of the ends of two wires or cables together.

■ **split bobbin winding**

a transformer winding technique where the primary and secondary are wound side-by-side on a bobbin with an insulation barrier between them.

■ **split phase start**

motor which employs a main winding and an auxiliary winding, which is called the starting winding. The windings are unlike and thereby "split" the single phase of the power supply by causing a phase displacement between the currents of the two windings thus producing a rotating field. After the motor has attained approximately 75% of rated speed, the starting winding is automatically disconnected by means of a centrifugal switch or by a relay. The motor then continues to run on a single oscillating field, which in conjunction with the rotation of the rotor, results in a rotating field effect. Since there is no rotating field, after the starting winding is de-energized, the rotation cannot be changed until the motor has come to rest or at least slowed down to the speed at which the automatic switch closes. Special starting switches are available as well as special reversing switches which have a means for shunting the open contacts of the automatic switch while the motor is running and thus permits the split phase motor to be reversed while rotating. This type of starting is found typically on single phase fractional motors.

■ **spot size**

the diameter of the circle formed by the cross section of the field of view of an optical instrument at a given distance.

■ **spur**

a substitution for the term 'Spurious Frequency Response.' The word 'spur' is used to refer to a frequency occurring at some point higher than the desired mode but lower than the next overtone.

■ **spurious error**

Random or erratic malfunction.

■ **square law dimming**

dimming with direct correlation between the position of the slider and the light perceived by the eyeis known as Square Law Dimming. With Square Law Dimming, gradual movement of the linear slide results in a proportional change in the perceived lighting level allowing for easy, precise adjustment of the light setting.

■ **square wave**

an excitation that consists of an abrupt on/off cycling of the voltage. This typically goes in both the positive and negative direction. A positive-only square wave would be typical of pulse excitation.

■ **squareness ratio**

the ratio of residual flux density to the maximum (saturation) flux density.

■ **squirrel cage**

a steel bracket mounted on a pole to support line conductors.

■ **SRF (Self Resonant Frequency)**

the frequency at which tile inductor;s distributed capacitance resonates with the inductance. It is at this frequency that the inductance is equal to the capacitance and they cancel each other. The inductor will act purely resistive with a high impedance at the SRF point. The distributed capacitance is caused by the turns of ~re layered on top of each other and around the core. This capacitance is in parallel to the inductance. At frequencies above the SRF, the capacitive reactance of the parallel combination will become the dominant component. Also, tile Q of the inductor is equal to zero at the SRF point since the inductive reactance is zero. The SRF is specified in Mhz and is listed as a minimum value on product data sheets (Also see **distributed capacitance**)

■ **SSR**

Solid State Relay (see **relay, solid state**).

■ **stability**

the maximum amount of frequency deviation of the oscillator. Stability includes the tolerance at 25° C; drift over operating temperature range; changes in input voltage; changes in load, shock, vibration; and aging.

■ stabilised shunt-wound motor

a stabilised shunt-wound motor is a direct-current motor in which the shunt field circuit is connected either in parallel with the armature circuit or to a separate source of excitation voltage and which also has a light series winding added to prevent a rise in speed or to obtain a slight reduction in speed with increase in load.

■ stabilsability

a dynamical system is stabilisable if all of its unstable modes are controllable. Also see **the dual concept of detectability**.

■ stable system

usually refers to systems whose poles all lie in the open left half plane. Such poles are associated with decaying exponentials and exponential sinusoids in the time domain. Also see **unstable system**.

■ stagnation pressure

the sum of the static and dynamic pressure.

■ standard electrode potential (E0)

the standard potential E0 of an electrode is the reversible emf between the normal hydrogen electrode and the electrode with all components at unit activity.

■ standardisation

a process of equalizing electrode potentials in one Standardising solution (buffer) so that potentials developed in unknown solutions can be converted to pH values.

■ standby current

amount of current consumed by the oscillator when it is in its standby mode.

■ standby function

a control function similar to the Enable/Disable function. In this case, the oscillator actually stops oscillating. This type of oscillator draws less current than an Enable/Disable type oscillator (when both are in their disabled states).

■ star

the most common network topology where each node is connected to a central point. This topology is preferred as the network continues to function even if one or more nodes are damaged or disconnected.

■ star system

a method of connecting three single transformers for three phase application.

■ starting current

amount of current drawn at the instant a motor is energised - in most cases much higher than that required for running. Same as locked rotor current.

■ starting torque

the torque or twisting force delivered by a motor at the instant it is energized. Starting torque is often higher than rated running or full load torque.

■ start-up time

the period from the instant voltage is applied to the oscillator until the oscillator output is stabilised.

■ **state estimator**

refers to systems which process input and output measurements in order to estimate the state of the system. Also see **kalman filter and observer.**

■ **state feedback**

refers to control laws which generate control signals on the basis of state information alone. Also referred to as a control law which exploits perfect information. Most of the literature todate has focussed on constant gain state feedback control laws; i.e. state feedback control laws which take on the form u =G x where u denotes an m-dimensional control, x denotes an n-dimensional state, and G is a constant m x n control gain matrix.

■ **state of a system**

refers to the minimum information required at a given instant to determine the future evolution (e.g. output) of the system given knowledge of the current and future inputs. Also called initial state.

■ **state variables**

set of variables which can be used to summarize the state of the system at any given time instant. Usually selected to be variables which are associated with energy storage within the system (e.g. capacitor voltages, inductor currents, spring positions, speed of masses, etc.).

■ **static calibration**

a calibration recording pressure versus output at fixed points at room temperature.

■ **static error band**

the error band applicable at room temperature.

■ **static pressure**

pressure of a fluid whether in motion or at rest. It can be sensed in a small hole drilled perpendicular to and flush with the flow boundaries so as not to disturb the fluid in any way.

■ **static scanning**

scanning method which generates periodic signals during movement; the signal periods and fractions thereof correspond to a definite linear or angular displacement.

■ **static unbalance**

Static unbalance is that condition of unbalance for which the central principal axis is displayed only parallel to the shaft axis.

■ **stator**

that part of an AC induction motor's magnetic structure which does not rotate. It usually contains the primary winding. The stator is made up of laminations with a large hole in the centre in which the rotor can turn; there are slots in the stator in which the windings for the coils are inserted.

■ **steady flow**

a flow rate in the measuring section of a flow line that does not vary significantly with time.

■ **steady state vibration**

that condition of vibration induced by an unchanging continuing periodic force.

■ **step change**

sudden change in a converter parameter. Typically used in referring to changes in output load or input line during converter testing.

■ **step down**

to reduce the voltage of a circuit, from a higher to a lower value, by means of a transformer.

■ **step down transformer**

when the secondary has a lower voltage than the primary.

■ **step response**

the step response of a system is the response of the system to a step function. Unless otherwise specified, a unit step function input under zero initial conditions is implied.

■ **step-down**

this refers to a transformer that has fewer turns of wire in the secondary than in the primary, which causes a decrease or step-down of the voltage.

■ **step-up**

this refers to a transformer that has more turns of wire in the secondary than in the primary, which causes an increase or step-up of the voltage.

■ **stiff line**

a condition where there is no significant impedance present in the AC mains feeding input power to a power supply. The input power supply does not change appreciably with load.

■ **stiffness**

the ratio of the force required to create a certain deflection or movement of a part expressed as (Force/deflection) lbs/in or grams/cm.

■ **stop bit**

a signal following a character or block that prepares the receiving device to receive the next character or block.

■ **stopband**

the part of the frequency spectrum that is subjected to specified attenuation of signal strength by a filter.

■ **storage temperature range**

range of ambient temperatures over which a component can be stored safely. See **operating temperature range**.

■ **strain**

when a material is distorted by forces acting on it, it is said to be strained. Strain is the ratio of change in dimension to original dimension.

■ **strain gauge**

a measuring element for converting force, pressure, tension, etc., into an electrical signal.

■ **strain relief**

a method of protecting the wire to contact point from flexing or pulling.

■ **stranded costs**

(See **Competition Transition Charge**)

■ **stranded wire (or conductor)**

multiple small AWG strands of wire that are put together to make a flexible wire with similar electrical properties as a similar solid wire. Stranded wires are usually used in data cabling.

■ **stress cones**

a physical protection placed over the external connections point on medium and high voltage motor leads. Stress cones are used to avoid di-electric breakdown of motor leads in the vicinity of the external connection. Stress cones generally require an oversized conduit box on large motors.

■ **string**

a sequence of characters.

■ **strouhal number**

a nondimensional parameter important in vortex meter design defined as: s = Fh/V where f = frequency, V = velocity, and h = a reference length

■ **substation**

a set of transformers that change the voltage of electrical energy to levels appropriate for end use

■ **successive approximation**

a technique used in A-D converters to measure an analogue signal. It compares the signal with progressively smaller values, each step getting nearer the actual voltage.

■ **sulphur dioxide (SO2)**

a corrosive gas produced both by nature and technology in nearly equal amounts. Burning fuels, such as coal and oil, that contain sulphur produces SO2. It is also produced from sea spray, organic decomposition and volcanic eruptions. When combined with water in the air, it produces a weak, corrosive sulphuric acid — an ingredient of acid rain. The control of SO_2 has been given the highest priority at utility companies.

■ **super cooling**

The cooling of a liquid below its freezing temperature without the formation of the solid phase.

■ **super heating**

1. the heating of a liquid above its boiling temperature without the formation of the gaseous phase. 2. The heating of the gaseous phase considerably above the boiling-point temperature to improve the thermodynamic efficiency of a system.

■ **supply current**

rated output current of a given device. Power switch devices have been designed to support a continuous load (supply) current of 0.6A at ambient temperature.

■ **supply voltage**

voltage level of the power switch input. Raychem power switch devices have been designed to operate using supply voltage levels from 3.0V to 5.5V.

■ **surface area**

the effective surface area of a typical wound core available to dissipate heat.

surface mount

refers to a package with pads that mount to the surface of the PCB.

surge

a large, momentary, increase in the voltage on a power line.

surge current

a current of short duration that occurs when power is first applied to capacitive loads or temperature dependent resistive loads such as tungsten or molybdenum heaters- usually lasting no more than several cycles.

surge protection

a capacitor device usually mounted in the conduit box to flatten the voltage surges that may occur as a result of lighting or a power supply surge (short-period peak). These surges could result in more than twice the rated voltage going to the windings and in turn cause winding damage.

suspension effect

the source of error due to varied reference liquid junction potential depending upon whether the electrodes are immersed in the supernatant fluid or deeper in the sediment. Normally encountered with solutions containing resins or charged colloids.

sustained outage

an electrical outage that lasts longer than two minutes.

SVGA

Super Video Graphics Array.

s-video

a video signal that separates the "Y" or Luma and "C" or chroma information.

swing

a term used to describe how inductance responds to changes in current, i.e. a 2:1 swing corresponds to an inductor which exhibits two times more inductance at very low current than it does at its maximum rated current. This would also correspond to the core operating at 50% of initial permeability (50% saturation).

swinging inductors

a special type of inductor that exhibits high inductance at low MMF and moderate inductance at high MMF. There are two popular techniques for accomplishing this: placing a common winding on a high permeability core and a low permeability core, and placing a staggered gap into a high permeability core.

switch

A switch is a multiport bridge that segregates different portions of a network for faster network access.

switch mode power supply

a power conversion technique that involves breaking the input power into pulses at a high frequency by switching it on and off and recombining these pulses at the output stage. Using this technique, an unregulated input voltage can be converted to one or more regulated output voltages at relatively high efficiencies.

switch, general use

a switch intended for use in general distribution and branch circuits. It is rated in amperes and is capable of interrupting its rated voltage.

switch, general-use snap

a type of general-use switch so constructed that it can be installed in flush device boxes or on outlet covers, or otherwise used in conjunction with wiring systems recognised by the National Electric Code.

switch, isolating

a switch intended for isolating an electrical circuit from the source of power. It has no interrupting rating and is intended to be operated only after the circuit has been opened by some other means.

switch, knife

a switch in which the circuit is closed by a moving blade engaging contact clips.

switch, motor-circuit

a switch, rated in horsepower, capable of interrupting the maximum operating overload current of a motor of the same horsepower rating as the switch at the rated voltage.

switch, transfer

a transfer switch is an automatic or nonautomatic device for transferring one or more load conductor connections from one power source to another.

switchboard

a large single panel, frame, or assembly of panels having switches, overcurrent, and other protective devices, buses, and usually instruments mounted on the face or back or both. Switchboards are generally accessible from the rear and from the front and are not intended to be installed in cabinets.

switched current

the maximum current level that can be reliably handled while opening and closing contacts.

Switched Virtual Circuit (SVC)

a virtual link, with variable end-points, established through an ATM network. With an SVC, the user defines the end-points when the call is initiated that are subsequently terminated at the end of the call. With a Permanent Virtual Circuit(PVC), the end-points are predefined by the network manager. A single virtual path may support multiple.

switching centre

a staffed substation, where all switching operations are communicated and logged, and the status of all electrical circuits are monitored.

switching frequency

the rate at which the DC input to a switching regulator is switched on and off.

switching regulator

a circuit that is designed to regulate the output voltage from a given unregulated input voltage by using a closed control loop design. The most common switching regulator types involve a magnetic component, such as an inductor or transformer, that is used to store and transfer energy to the output by having the current switched on and off.

■ **switching regulator**

a circuit that is designed to regulate the output voltage, from a given input voltage, by using a closed control loop design. The most common switching regulator types involve a magnetic component, such as an inductor or transformer, that is used to store and transfer energy to the output by having the current switched on and off (Also see **boost regulator and buck regulator**)

■ **switch-leg**

that part of a circuit run from a lighting outlet box where a luminaire or lampholder is installed down to an outlet box that contains the wall switch that turns the light or other load on or off: it is a control leg of the branch circuit.

■ **symmetrical transmission**

transmission in which a channel sends and receives data with the same signaling rate.

■ **symmetry**

a measure of the uniformity of the output waveform.

■ **SYNC**

a abbreviation for Synchronising, as in synchronising pulses. The

timing pulses in a video signal which identify lines, fields and frames.

■ **synchronous motor**

a motor which operates at a constant speed up to full load. The rotor speed is equal to the speed of the rotating magnetic field of the stator; there is no slip. There are two (2) major types reluctance and permanent magnet on synchronous motors. A synchronous motor is often used where the exact speed of a motor must be maintained.

■ **Synchronous Optical Network (SONET)**

a Bellcore and ANSI standard that defines transmission of synchronous and time sensitive (ex: real time video) information. SONET provides a way for worldwide carriers to connect equipment.

■ **synchronous speed**

the speed of the rotating magnetic field set up by the stator winding of an induction motor. In a synchronous motor the rotor locks into step with the rotating magnetic field, and the motor is said to run at synchronous speed. Approximately the speed of the motor with no load on it.

■ **sync-on-green**

an RGB signal format in which the sync information for all three channels is included on the green channel.

■ **syntax**

The rules governing the structure of a language.

system

an operator which maps input signals u to output signals y. This concept represents a natural extension to the concept of a function.

system damage voltage

maximum voltage across a SiBar device at breakdown measured under a specified voltage rate of rise and current rate of rise. Synonyms: Breakover Voltage

systematic error

reproducible measuring deviation, which can be compensated for by e.g. computation.

t (temperature codes)

See **N.E.C. Temperature Codes**

t frame

current NEMA designation identifying AC induction motor frames. (NEMA has dimension tables which offer standard frame measurements) Replaced the previous standard "U" frame in 1965.

T.C.X.O

the abbreviation for 'Temperature Compensated Crystal Oscillator.' Such an oscillator contains a temperature sensing network that adjusts the output frequency, thereby allowing the frequency to remain constant over a specified temperature range.

t1

digital transmission facility operating with a nominal bandwidth of 1.544 Mbps. Also known as Digital Signal Level 1 (D1). Composed of 24 DS-0 channels in many cases.

The T1 digital transmission system if the primary digital communication system in North America.

t3

digital transmission facility operating at 45 Mbps bandwidth. Composed of 28 DS-1 channels in many cases. Also known as DS-3.

TA

Tested Amps on a meter.

tachometer

a small generator normally used as a rotational speed sensing device. Tachometers are typically attached to the output shaft of DC or AC inverter motors requiring close speed regulation. The tachometer feeds its signal to a control which adjusts its output to the DC motor or AC inverter motors accordingly (called 'closed loop feedback' control).

talker

a device on the GPIB (general purpose interface bus) that sends information to a Listener on the bus.

tank circuit

parallel resonant circuit containing only a coil and a capacitor. Both the coil and capacitor store electrical energy for part of each cycle.

tantalum capacitor

electrolytic capacitor having a tantalum foil anode. Able to have a large capacity in a small package.

tap

electrical connection to some point

other than at the ends of a resistor or inductor.

■ **tap line**

a line that has one source of feed.

■ **tape**

a recording media for data or computer programs. Tape can be in permanent form, such as perforated paper tape, or erasable, such as magnetic tape. Generally, tape is used as a mass storage medium, in magnetic form, and has a much higher storage capacity than disk storage, but it takes much longer to write or recover data from tape than from a disk.

■ **tape and reel**

refers to the packaging method used to accommodate automated pick & place equipment.

■ **tape wound cores**

cores made by rolling strips of alloy iron into a toroidal shape. The metal strips have a precisely controlled thickness, which are coated with a very thin insulating material to prevent the metal in the layers to make contact with each other. The finished cores have an outside coating to protect the metal layers and they are offered in a variety of material mixes. Tape wound cores are capable of storing high amounts of energy and contain a high permeability. Their major disadvantage is that they are relatively expensive when compared to other core types.

■ **tapered**

non-uniform distribution of resistance per unit length throughout

the element of a potentiometer.

■ **tariff**

a collection of public schedules detailing utility cost-of-service rates, rules, service territory, and terms of service that a regulated utility files with its public utilities commission for official approval. Tariffs that have been approved by a public utilities commission are binding legal documents and must be made available to the public. In effect, they constitute the contract between a utility and its consumers.

■ **TDM**

Time Division Multiplexing

■ **TDMA**

Time Division Multiple Access

■ **technician**

expert in troubleshooting circuit and system malfunctions. Along with a thorough knowledge of test equipment and how to use it to diagnose problems, the technician is also familiar with how to repair or replace faulty components. Technicians basically translate theory into action.

■ **Technischer Uberwachungs-Verin (TUV)**

organisation approved for testing products to VDE standards. US-based companies often use TUV in place of VDE because they hae established facilities in the US.

■ **teflon**

a fluorocarbon polymer used for insulation of electrical wires (trademark of DuPont Company).

■ **telecommunications**

communications over a distance, generally by electronic means. Today it is possible to communicate with most countries by telephone cable, or by satellite or microwave link, with over 100,000 simultaneous conversations and several television channels being carried by the latest satellites. Integrated-Services Digital Network ISDN) makes videophone and high-quality fax possible; the world's first large-scale centre of ISDN began operating in Japan 1988. ISDN is a system that transmit voice and image data on a single transmission line by changing them into digital signals. The chief method of relaying long-distance calls on land is microwave radio transmission.

■ **telecommunications closet**

enclosed space for containing telecommunications equipment, cable terminations and cross connects.

■ **telecommunications transformers**

also referred to as broadband transformers, these are transformers specialized for connecting a piece of equipment to the phone line or telephone network. Its function is to isolate the equipment from the phone line, improve common mode noise rejection, and match different impedances.

■ **telecommuter**

Person who performs work at home while linked to the office by means of a telecommunications-equipped computer system.

■ **telegraphy**

communication between two points by sending and receiving a series of current pulses either through wire or by radio.

■ **telemetry**

transmission of instrument readings to a remote location either by wire or by radio.

■ **telephone**

apparatus designed to convert sound waves into electrical waves which are sent to and reproduced ata distant point.

■ **telephone line**

wires existing between subscribers and central stations in a telephone system.

■ **telephony**

telecommunications system involving the transmission of speech information, allowing two or more persons to communicate verbally.

■ **teletypewriter**

electric typewriter that like a teleprinter can produce coded signals corresponding to the keys pressed or print characters corresponding to the coded signals received.

■ **television**

system that converts both audio and visual information into corresponding electrical signals which are then transmitted through wires or by radio waves to a receiver which reproduces the original information.

■ **TELEX**

Teletypewriter Exchange Service.

■ TEMPCO

abbreviation for 'Temperature Coefficient': the error introduced by a change in temperature. Normally expressed in /°C or ppm/°C.

■ temperature

1. state of hotness or coldness of a body, and the condition that determines whether or not it will transfer heat to, or receive heat from, another body according to the laws of thermodynamics. It is measured in degrees Celsius (before 1948 called centigrade), Kelvin or Fahrenheit. The normal temperature of the human body is about 98.4F/36.9C. Variation by more than degree or so indicates ill health, a rise signifying excessive activity (usually due to infection), and a decrease signifying deficient heat production (usually due to lessened vitality).

2. has direct bearing on the life of a given motor and when considering life expectancy, the following application considerations that affect the motor's operating temperature, should be taken into account

1. Bearing
2. Lubricants
3. Duty Cycle
4. Radial Loading
5. Axial Loading
6. Mounting
7. Enclosure
8. Ambient Temperature
9. Ventilation

As a general rule of thumb each 10fC increase in total temperature over the maximum permissible to the motor insulation system halves its life. Bearing or gear lubricant life is halved for every 25fF (approx. 14fC) increase in temperature. Heat eventually causes deterioration of most lubricants and seals leading to leakage and increased friction.

■ Temperature Coefficient (T.C.)

in a capacitor, the rating which determines the change in capacitance corresponding to a given change in operating temperature. It is usually expressed as the change in capacitance per unit of capacitance per degree Celsius.

■ temperature coefficient of frequency

rate at which frequency changes with temperature.

■ temperature coefficient of inductance

(Tc of L)Is the value of inductance change as a function of temperature exposure, normally expressed in parts per million per degrees Celsius. This is a calculation comparing inductance at a reference temperature (25 degrees C, room ambient) to the extremes and other temperatures within operating range. Can be called Percent Delta L. or Temperature Stability: the lower the change the better for most applications.

■ temperature derating

reducing the output power of a power supply with increasing temperature to maintain reliable operation.

■ **temperature error**

the maximum change in output, at any measurand value within the specified range, when the transducer temperature is changed from room temperature to specified temperature extremes.

■ **Temperature Factor (TF)**

the fractional change in initial permeability over a temperature range divided by the initial permeability.

■ **temperature range**

the ambient temperature range of the air (or other medium) surrounding a polyswitch device under normal operating conditions.

■ **temperature range, compensated**

the range of ambient temperatures within which all tolerances specified for Thermal Zero Shift and Thermal Sensitivity Shift are applicable (temperature error).

■ **temperature range, operable**

the range of ambient temperatures, given by their extremes, within which the transducer may be operated. Exceeding compensated range may require recalibration.

■ **temperature rise**

some of the electrical energy losses inherent in motors are converted to heat causing some of the motor parts to heat up when the motor is running. The heated parts are at a higher temperature than the air surrounding them thereby causing a rise above room (ambient) temperature.

it is important to match the proper motor and insulation system (NEMA temp. codes) to the appropriate ambient temperature. If a motor has been built with greater than 1.0 service factor then it can run at a temperature some what higher than the motor's rated operating temperature. In all cases, the actual insulation thermal capability usually is higher than the motor's operating temperature to allow for any excessive heat areas. This is called hot spot allowance. (See Insulation Systems for NEMA standard temperature codes.) Each temperature code has an associated temperature rise which when added to the ambient and hot spot should not exceed the temperature handing of the insulation system.

■ **temperature tests**

tests conducted to determine the temperature rise of certain parts of a motor above the ambient temperature, when operating under specific conditions.

■ **temperature, maximum ambient operating**

the highest ambient temperature at which a circuit is expected to operate.

■ **temporary magnet**

an artificial magnet that loses its magnetism after the magnetising force is removed. Soft iron is an example of a temporary magnet.

■ **temporary power pole (tpp)**

a-self supporting pole of timber

of proper dimensions, provided by the customer, to support SCE's service wires and meter. It is generally used for construction purposes.

■ **tera**

(T) Metric prefix that represents 10^{12}.

■ **thermal conductivity**

given materials ability to conduct heat, which is the time rate for heat transfer (via conduction) across a unit material thickness of 1 meter and when the temperature differential of the two opposite faces is 1 degree K.

■ **terminal**

an input/output device used to enter data into a computer and record the output.

■ **terminal chamber**

point of attachment for line and load wires to attach to any "A" base meter.

■ **terminated/termination/ terminator**

an impedance used to terminate a transmission line. For example, cables used for video distribution should be terminated with a 75 ohm resistor (terminator) at the last connector on the receiving end if it is not already terminated internally.

■ **termination (mechanical)**

the process of installing a connector onto a fiber or copper cable.

■ **termination impedance**

the impedance that should be pre-

sented to the source and load side of the filter to ensure proper performance.

■ **tesla**

standard unit of magnetic flux density equal to one weber per square meter. The previously used unit of flux density was the gauss, which was equal to one magnetic line per square centimeter.

■ **test**

sequence of operations intended to verify the correct operation or malfunctioning of a piece of equipment or system.

■ **test frequency**

is the industry/military standard for testing a range of inductances. It is not intended as the application frequency. Expressed in megahertz (MHz) or kilohertz (kHz)

■ **test set**

a device used to measure the frequency and resistance characteristics of a quartz crystal unit. Often called a 'crystal impedance meter,' abbreviated as 'C.I.M.'

■ **test, humidity aging**

a test described in RaychemÕs PS300 publication in which the resistance of a polyswitch device at room temperature is measured before and after aging at an elevated temperature (e.g., 40°C) and high humidity (e.g., 95% RH) for an extended time (e.g., 1000 hours).

■ **test, passive aging**

a test described in RaychemÕs PS300 publication in which the resistance of a polyswitch device at room temperature is measured before and after aging at an elevated temperature (e.g., 70°C or 85°C) for an extended time (e.g., 1000 hours).

■ **test, solvent resistance**

a test described in RaychemÕs PS300 publication to test the durability of the markings on polyswitch devices when exposed to various solvents.

■ **test, thermal shock**

a test in which the resistance of a polyswitch device at room temperature is measured before and after a temperature cycling treatment (e.g., cycled 10 times between 55°C and +125°C).

■ **tests**

a variety of tests are conducted to ensure motor performance, efficiency, and manufacturing integrity.

■ **the utility reform network (turn)**

this San Francisco-based consumer group was founded more than 25 years ago. It claims to advocate for California utility consumers by participating in CPUC proceedings and other activities.

■ **therm**

a unit of energy equivalent to 100,000 BTUs. Usually used as a measure of the heat energy from burning natural gas (or methane).

■ **thermal**

coefficient of resistance. The

change in resistance of a semiconductor per unit change in temperature, over a specific range of temperature.

■ **thermal coefficient of resistance**

the change in resistance of a semiconductor per unit change in temperature over a specific range of temperature.

■ **thermal conductivity**

given materials ability to conduct heat, which is the time rate for heat transfer (via conduction) across a unit material thickness of 1 meter and when the temperature differential of the two opposite faces is 1 degree K.

■ **thermal derating**

the change in the hold current and trip current of a polyswitch device that takes place as there is a change in the ambient temperature of the air (or other medium) surrounding the device. An increase in ambient temperature decreases the hold current (and the trip current). A decrease in ambient temperature increases the trip current (and the hold current).

■ **thermal emf**

See **seebeck emf**

■ **thermal expansion**

an increase in size due to an increase in temperature expressed in units of an increase in length or increase in size per degree, i.e. inches/inch/degree C.

■ **thermal gasket**

flexible pad or wafer with a very

low thermal resistance that is put between a power module baseplate and heat sink to ensure high thermal conductivity across the junction

■ **thermal gradient**

the distribution of a differential temperature through a body or across a surface.

■ **thermal joint compound**

a fluid or paste spread between the mating surfaces of a power device baseplate and a heat sink or system chassis.

■ **thermal protection**

feature that shuts the converter down if the internal tempurature exceeds preset limits. Also called thermal shutdown.

■ **thermal protector (inherent)**

an inherent overheating protective device which is responsive to motor temperature and which, when properly applied to a motor, protects the motor against dangerous overheating due to overload or failure to start. This protection is available with either manual or automatic reset.

■ **thermal relay**

relay activated by a heating element.

■ **thermal resistance**

measure of a given material;s opposition to the flow of heat. Units are in degrees C/W.

■ **thermal resistivity**

measure of a materials ability to

impede the flow of heat. Typically given in degrees C T/W, where T is the material thickness and W is the power flowing through the material in watts.

■ **thermal runaway**

problem that can develop in an amplifier when an increase in temperature causes an increase in collector current. The increase in collector current causes a further increase in temperature and so on. Unless the circuit is designed to prevent this condition, the device can be driven into saturation.

■ **thermal sensitivity shift**

the sensitivity shift due to changes of the ambient temperature from room temperature to the specified limits of the compensated temperature range.

■ **thermal shock test**

a test in which the resistance of a polyswitch device at room temperature is measured before and after a temperature cycling treatment (e.g., cycled 10 times between Đ55°C and +125°C).

■ **thermal stability**

the ability of a circuit to maintain stable characteristics in spite of increased temperature.

■ **thermal zero shift**

an error due to changes in ambient temperature in which the zero pressure output shifts. Thus, the entire calibration curve moves in a parallel displacement.

■ **thermionic emission**

the liberation of electrons from a

solid metal as a result of heat (thermal energy).

■ thermistor

a temperature-sensing element composed of sintered semiconductor material which exhibits a large change in resistance proportional to a small change in temperature. Thermistors usually have negative temperature coefficients. Thermocouple Type Material (ANSI Symbol)
J Iron/Constantan
K   CHROMEGA®/ ALOMEGA®
T Copper/Constantan
E CHROMEGA®/Constantan
R Platinum/Platinum 13% Rhodium
S Platinum/Platinum 10% Rhodium
B Platinum 6% Rhodium/Platinum30% Rhodium
G* Tungsten/Tungsten 26% Rhenium
C* Tungsten 5% Rhenium/Tungsten 26% Rhenium
D* Tungsten 3% Rhenium/Tungsten 150 Rhenium
*Not ANSI symbols.

■ thermistor-thermally sensitive resistor

a semiconductor used to measure temperature; can be attached to an alarm or meter to detect motor overheating.

■ thermocouple

popular temperature sensor because of its low cost, wide operating range and ruggedness. Consists of two dissimilar metals joined together, making a continuous loop. When one junction has a dif-

ferent temperature from the other an electromotive force (voltage) occurs. There are several types of thermocouples, constructed from different metals and with differing temperature ranges and accuracies.

■ thermocouple-thermal detection device

a temperature detecting device made of two dissimilar metals which generate a voltage as a function of temperature. Thermocouples can be attached to a meter or alarm to detect overheating of motor windings or bearings.

■ thermodynamics

branch of physics dealing with the transformation of heat into and from other forms of energy. It is the basis of the study of the efficient working of engines, such as the steam and internal-combustion engines. The three laws of thermodynamics are 1) energy can be neither created nor destroyed, heat and mechanical work being mutually convertible; 2) it is impossible for an unaided self-acting machine to convey heat from one body to another at higher temperature; and 3) it is impossible by any procedure, no matter who idealized, to reduce any system to the absolute zero of temperature ()K/-460F) in a finite number of operations. Put into mathematical form, these laws have widespread applications in physics and chemistry.

■ thermometry

relating to the measuring of temperature.

thermopile

an arrangement of thermocouples in series such that alternate junctions are at the measuring temperature and the reference temperature. This arrangement amplifies the thermoelectric voltage. Thermopiles are usually used as infrared detectors in radiation pyrometry.

thermostat

units applied directly to the motor's windings which senses winding temperature and may automatically break the circuit in an overheating situation.

thermowell

a closed-end tube designed to protect temperature sensors from harsh environments, high pressure, and flows. They can be installed into a system by pipe thread or welded flange and are usually made of corrosion-resistant metal or ceramic material depending upon the application.

thevenin's theorem

theorem that replaces any complex network with a single voltage source in series with a single resistance.

thick film resistor

fixed value resistor consisting of thick-film resistive element made from metal particles and glass powder.

thick-film capacitor

capacitor consisting of two thick-film layers of conductive film separated by a deposited thick-layer dialectric film.

thin film capacitor

capacitor in which both the electrodes and the dialectric are deposited in layers on a substrate.

thin film detector

(TFD) A temperature detector containing a thin layer of platinum and used for precise temperature readings.

thomson effect

when current flows through a conductor within a thermal gradient, a reversible absorption or evolution of heat will occur in the conductor at the gradient boundaries.

three phase supply

AC supply that consists of three AC voltages 120° out of phase with each other.

three-phase

a generator or circuit delivering these voltages that are one third of a cycle apart in reaching their maximum value.

three-phase bank

two or more single transformers connected together to serve a three-phase circuit.

three-phase motor

an alternating current motor that is operated from a three—phase circuit.

three-terminal regulator

regulator packaged in a standard 3-terminal transistor package. These devices can be a switching type or a linear shunt or series regulator.

■ **threshold**

minimum point at which an effect is produced or detected.

■ **threshold voltage**

for an enhancement MOSFET, the minimum gate source voltage required for conduction of source drain current.

■ **throughput**

number of results produced per unit time.

■ **thrust bearings**

special bearings used to handle higher than normal axial forces exerted on the shaft of the motor as is the case with some fan or pump blade mountings.

■ **thyristor**

a term used to classify all four layer semiconductot devices. SCRs and triacs are examples of thyristors.

■ **tidal energy**

refers to the production of electricity using the regular ebb and flow of the ocean tides. The tides are directed through reversible turbines in a dam which turn generators to produce electricity.

■ **time constant**

the time constant tau associated with a decaying exponential exp(-st) is defined by the relationship: tau = 1/Re(s) where Re(s) denotes the real part of the complex quantity s. Tau is measured using the same units that t is measured in. the above exponential is said to take approximately 5 tau time units

(or 5 time constants) to decay to zero. This terminology is commonly used by engineers. It should be noted that values of s close to (far from) the origin of the complex s-plane (i.e. s = 0) correspond to large (small) time constants.

■ **time delay**

refers to a system whose output y is always the applied input u delayed (shifted) by a non-negative quantity delta where delta is the size of the time delay; i.e. y(t) = u(t delta). Such a system is LTI and has a transfer function given by exp(-s delta).

■ **Time Division Multiplexing**

(TDM) transmission of two or more signals on the same path, but at different times.

■ **time stamp**

information added to data to indicate the time at which it was collected.

■ **time-domain analysis**

a method of representing a waveform by plotting amplitude over time.

■ **time-of-use**

a TOU rate gives customers the option of operating during off-peak periods to reduce energy costs. SCE off-peak hours are from 6 PM to 10 AM the following day.

■ **time-to-trip**

the time needed, from the onset of a fault current, to trip a polyswitch device. For any particular type of polyswitch device, trip time depends upon the size of the fault current and the ambient temperature. The higher the fault current and/or the higher the temperature, the shorter the trip time. Synonyms: Trip Time,TtT

■ **TNC**

a threaded type of BNC coaxial connector.

■ **toggle switch**

spring loaded switch that is put in one of two positions either on or off.

■ **token ring**

a networking standard that utilises a ring topology. Information is put onto the ring which is then passed (Token Passing) to the different stations. The amount of time that a station possesses the token is variable which gives some users priority on the network. Token Ring was Standardised by IEEE under the 802.5 standard.

■ **tolerance**

permissable deviation from a specified value normally expressed as a percentage.

■ **topology**

The design type of a converter, indicative of the configuration of switching transistors, utilisation of the transformer, and type of filtering. Examples of topologies are Flyback, Forward, Half-Bridge, Full Bridge, and Resonant.

■ **toroid**

a core that has a donut shaped surface. Toroidal cores are available in many magnetic core materials. Characteristics of toroidal inductors include self-shielding due to a closed magnetic path, efficient energy transfer, high coupling between windings, and early saturation.

■ **toroidal coil**

coil wound on a doughnut shaped core.

■ **toroidal inductor**

an inductor constructed by placing a winding(s) on a core that has a donut shaped surface. Toroidal cores are available in many magnetic core materials within the four basic types: Ferrite, Powdered iron, Alloy and High Flux, and Tape Wound. Characteristics of toroidal inductors include: self shielding (closed magnetic path), efficient energy transfer, high coupling between windings and early saturation.

■ **torque**

turning force delivered by a motor or gearmotor shaft, usually expressed in lbs. ft derived by completing H.P. x 5250/RPM = full load torque.

■ **torsional stiffness**

rotational rigidity of a precision coupling governing the reversal error of a rotary encoder.

■ **totally -enclosed air-to-air-cooled machine**

a totally enclosed machine cooled by circulating internal air through a heat exchanger which, in turn, is cooled by circulating external air. Provided with an air-to-air heat exchanger for cooling ventilating air and fan or fans integral with rotor shaft or separate, for circulating external air.

■ **totally -enclosed enclosure**

a motor enclosure which prevents free exchange of air between the inside and the outside of the enclosure but is not airtight. Different methods of cooling can be used with this enclosure.

■ **totally -enclosed fan-cooled enclosure**

provides for exterior cooling by means of a fan(s) integral with the machine, but external to the enclosed parts.

■ **totally- enclosed non-ventilated enclosure**

has no provisions for external cooling to the enclosing parts. The motor is cooled by heat radiation from the exterior surfaces to the surrounding atmosphere.

■ **totally-enclosed pipe ventilated machine**

a totally-enclosed machine except for openings so arranged that inlet and outlet ducts or pipes may be connected to them for the admission and discharge of ventilating air. Air may be circulated by means integral with the machine or by means external to and not a part of the machine. In latter case, these machines shall be known as separately-forced-ventilated machines.

■ **totally-enclosed water air-cooled machine**

a totally-enclosed machine cooled by circulating air which, in turn, is cooled by circulating water. Provided with water-cooled heat exchanger for cooling ventilating air and fan or fans, integral with rotor shaft or separate, for circulating ventilating air.

■ **tracking**

a characteristic in a multiple output power supply where any changes in the output voltage of one output caused by line, load, and/or temperature are proportional to similar changes in accompanying outputs.

■ **transceiver**

a device used to change one media type to another. Transceivers usually get their power from the NIC.

■ **transconductance**

also called mutual conductance. Ratio of a change in output current to the change in input voltage that caused it.

■ **transducer**

a device (or medium) that converts energy from one form to another. The term is generally applied to devices that take physical phenomenon (pressure, temperature, humidity, flow, etc.) and convert it to an electrical signal.

■ **transducer vibration**

generally, any device which converts movement, either shock or steady state vibration, into an electrical signal proportional to the movement; a sensor.

■ **transformer**

a passive device that changes voltage, current, or impedance to the required parameters. This is usually done by placing two or more windings around a soft magnetic core. Applying a voltage to the primary winding will produce a magnetic field in the core, and in turn induce a voltage in the secondary winding(s).

■ **transformer coupling**

also called inductive coupling. Coupling of two circuits by means of mutual inductance provided by a transformer.

■ **transformer lines**

wires or cables through which high voltage electric power is moved from point to point.

■ **transformer oil**

oil used in a transformer to insulate the windings and carry- away the heat.

■ **transformer ratio**

the ratio of primary to the secondary voltages.

■ **transient**

spike or step change in a converter parameter. Commonly used in describing input line and output load characteristics.

■ **transient recovery time**

time required for a converter output to return to within specified limits following a step change in output load current. Expressed as a percentage of rated value.

■ **transient suppression**

the use of special devices to minimise the effects of transients in electronic circuits. Transient suppression devices include the metal oxide varistor (MOV), semiconductor transient voltage suppressor (TVS) and gas tube.

■ **transient vibration**

a temporary vibration or movement of a mechanical system.

■ **transistor**

term derived from 'transfer resistor.' Semiconductor device that can be used as an amplifier or as an electronic switch.

■ **transition cost balancing account (TCBA)**

the TCBA tracks the stranded costs and the revenues received from all sources to pay off those costs.

■ **transition region**

the part of the spectrum between the passband and the stopband.

■ **transitional flow**

flow between laminar and turbulent flow, usually between a pipe Reynolds number of 2000 and 4000.

■ **transmission**

sending of information.

■ **transmission controal protocol/internet protocol**

a reliable, full duplex, connection-oriented end to end transport protocol running on top of IP.

■ **transmission line**

high-voltage conductor used to carry electrical power from one place to another.

■ **transmission system**

see **power grid**.

■ **transmitter (two-wire)**

1. a device which is used to transmit data from a sensor via a two-wire current loop. The loop has an external power supply and the transmitter acts as a variable resistor with respect to its input signal. 2. A device which translates the low level output of a sensor or transducer to a higher level signal suitable for transmission to a site where it can be further processed.

■ **transparent lan service**

service offered by a provider that is used to connect LANs at geographically separated sites. 'Transparent' means the connection is invisible to the user and typically runs at the same speed as the LANs.

■ **TRI**

Telephony Return Interface

■ **triac**

bidirectional gate controlled thyristor similar to an SCR, but capable of conducting in both directions. Provides full wave control of AC power.

■ **triangular wave**

a repeating wave that has equal positive going and negative going ramps. The ramps have linear rates of change with time.

■ **triaxial cable**

a cable with three conductors: one conductor surrounded by an inner shield and an isolated outer shield. Generally, the inner shield is connected to a guard potential and the outer shield to signal LOW or ground.

■ **triboelectric noise**

the generation of electrical charges caused by layers of cable insulation. This is especially troublesome in high impedance accelerometers.

■ **trigger**

an external stimulus that initiates one or more instrument functions. Trigger stimuli include; a front panel button (TAKE), an external input voltage pulse.

■ **triggering**

initiation of an action in a circuit which then functions for a predetermined time. Example: The duration of one sweep in a cathode ray tube.

■ **trim sensitivity**

a measure of the incremental fractional frequency change for an incremental change in the value of load capacitance. Trim sensitivity (S) is expressed in terms of PPM/pF and is calculated with the following equation where (C_t) is the sum of the shunt capacitance (C_O) and the load capacitance (C_1).

■ trimmer

small value variable capacitor, resistor or inductor used to fine tune a larger value.

■ trip

switching of a polyswitch device from a low resistance to a high resistance. In its low-resistance state, the device permits normal currents to flow in a circuit. Occurrence of a fault drives the device to its high-resistance (or trippedÓ) state, and this reduces the current in the circuit to a low level.

■ trip current

the smallest steady state current that, if passed through a polyswitch device, will cause the device to trip, under specified conditions. Synonyms: IT

■ trip cycle

the tripping and resetting of a polyswitch device under specified conditions.

■ trip cycle life

the number of trip cycles that a polyswitch device will undergo without failure, with failure being defined in a specified way.

■ trip time

the time needed, from the onset of a fault current, to trip a polyswitch device. For any particular type of polyswitch device, trip time depends upon the size of the fault current and the ambient temperature. The higher the fault current and/or the higher the temperature, the shorter the trip time. Synonyms: Time-to-Trip, TtT

■ triple point

The temperature and pressure at which solid, liquid, and gas phases of a given substance are all present simultaneously in varying amounts.

■ tri-stage matrix

a switching architecture that utilises input stages, mid-stages and output stages in an efficient multi-stage matrix. Larger switching arrays are better served by this type of design since multiple signal paths are available for redundancy, the number of actual hardware signal crosspoints is reduced, and the physical size and cost of the unit is dramatically reduced. This design is not cost effective in switching arrays smaller than 32x32.

■ tri-state

the ability to turn the output on or off using pin one for control. The output will go to a high impedance when disabled, which facilitates the use of Auto Test Equipment (ATE). Note: Tri-state may be substituted for non-tri-state if pin #1 is left open or held high.

■ trivalent element

one having three valence electrons. Used as an impurity in semiconductor material to produce p-type material. Most commonly used trivalent elements are: Aluminium, Gallium and Boron.

■ **troubleshooting**

systematic approach to locating the cause of a fault in an electronic circuit or system.

■ **true power**

in an AC circuit, true power is the actual power consumed. It is distinguished from apparent power by eliminating the reactive power component that may be present.

■ **true rms**

the true root-mean-square value of an AC or AC-plus-DC signal, often used to determine power of a signal. For a perfect sine wave, the RMS value is 1.11072 times the rectified average value, which is utilised for low-cost metering. For significantly non-sinusoidal signals, a true RMS converter is required.

■ **truncation**

rejection of the final digits in a number, thus lessening the precision but not necessarily the accuracy.

■ **TTL**

Transistor-To-Transistor Logic. A form of solid state logic which uses only transistors to form the logic gates.

■ **TTL logic**

abbreviation for Transistor-Transistor Logic, a very typical medium speed digital technology.

■ **ttl unit load**

A load with TTL voltage levels, which will draw 40 μA for a logic 1 and -1.6 mA for a logic 0.

■ **ttl-compatible**

for digital input circuits, a logic 1 is obtained for inputs of 2.0 to 5.5 V which can source 40 μA, and a logic 0 is obtained for inputs of 0 to 0.8 V which can sink 1.6 mA. For digital output signals, a logic 1 is represented by 2.4 to 5.5 V with a current source capability of at least 400 μA; and a logic 0 is represented by 0 to 0.6 V with a current sink capability of at least 16 mA.

■ **TTT**

the time needed, from the onset of a fault current, to trip a polyswitch device. For any particular type of polyswitch device, trip time depends upon the size of the fault current and the ambient temperature. The higher the fault current and/or the higher the temperature, the shorter the trip time. Synonyms: Time-to-Trip, Trip Time

■ **t-type thermocouple**

copper-constantan thermocouple with a temperature range of -200 to 400 °C.

■ **tube cooled**

a motor in which heat is dissipated by air-to-air heat exchange.

■ **tuned circuit**

circuit that can have its component values adjusted so that it responds to one selected frequency and rejects all others.

■ **tunnel diode**

heavily doped junction diode that has negative resistance in the forward direction of its operating range.

■ **turbine**

engine in which steam, water, gas or air (see windmill) is made to spin a rotating shaft by pushing on angled blades, like a fan. Turbines are among the most powerful machines. Steam turbines are used to drive generators in power stations and ships' propellers; water turbines spin the generators in hydroelectric power.

■ **turbulent flow**

when forces due to inertia are more significant than forces due to viscosity. This typically occurs with a Reynolds number in excess of 4000.

■ **turn ratio**

the ratio of the primary voltage (or turns) to the secondary voltage (or turns)

■ **turn-off time**

sum of storage time and fall time.

■ **turn-on time**

sum of delay time and rise time.

■ **turnover temperature**

the temperature at which the frequency is at the top of the parabolic curve.

■ **turns ratio**

ratio of the number of turns in the secondary winding of a trans-

former to the number of turns in the primary winding.

■ **twinaxial**

an offshoot from coaxial cabling. Two centre conductors with one dielectric and braided shielding.

■ **twinaxial cable**

a cable with three conductors: one twisted pair of conductors surrounded by an outer shield.

■ **twinning**

a condition existing within a quartz stone wherein the optic and/or the electric axis suddenly reverses its natural order of polarity.

■ **twisted pair**

cable consisting of two 18 to 24 AWG (American Wire gauge) solid copper strands twisted around each other. The twisting provides a measure of protection from electromagnetic and radio-frequency interference.

■ **two phase**

two repeating waveforms having a phase difference of 90°.

■ **two-location dimming**

allows full-range dimming from two different locations.

■ **typical**

error is within plus or minus one standard deviation (±1%) of the nominal specified value, as computed from the total population.

■ **UADSL**

universal ADSL

■ UDP

User Datagram Protocol

■ UL

Underwriters Laboratories, Inc. An independent laboratory that establishes standards for commercial and industrial products.

■ ul listed

a product adhering to standards of Underwriters Laboratories, an independent, non-profit testing laboratory Organised for the purpose of investigating products and materials with respect to hazards affecting life and property.

■ ultraviolet

that portion of the electromagnetic spectrum below blue light (380 nanometers).

■ UMTS

Universal Mobile Telecommunications Service

■ unbalance

that condition which exists in a rotor when vibratory force or motion is imparted to its bearings as a result of centrifugal forces.

■ unbalance tolerance

the unbalance tolerance with respect to a radial plane (measuring plane or correction plane) is that amount of unbalance which is specified as the maximum below which the state of unbalance is considered acceptable.

■ un-balanced

a transmission circuit with an impedance to ground. See differen-

tial input. This is also referred to as a single-ended transmission line. Most analog signals over 100MHz are single ended. The compliment to this type of transmission line is differential.

■ uncertainty

refers to the fact that the following is never known exactly: plant dynamics and parameters (e.g. actuator dynamics and parameters), sensor dynamics and parameters, functional form of disturbances, disturbance parameters, functional form of sensor noise, sensor noise parameters. Such uncertainty is the main reason for needing feedback control laws. To illustrate the effects of uncertainty, consider that a typical swept-wing transport at high subsonic speeds will experience a (1) reduction in wing lift-curve slope of about 20%, (2) reduction in tail pitching moment contribution of about 30%, (3) reduction in elevator effectiveness of about 50%, and a (4) 10% MAC (mean aerodynamic chord) forward shift in the wing aerodynamic centre (this affects stability) due to flexiblity along the longitudinal axis.

■ undamped poles

refers to a set of complex conjugate poles on the imaginary axis. Such poles have a zero damping ratio zeta and are associated with undamped sinusoidal oscillations in the time domain.

■ underdamped poles

refers to a set of complex conjugate poles which are stable (i.e. lie in the open left half plane). Such poles have a damping ratio zeta which lies in the interval (0, 1) and are associated with exponentially decaying sinusoids in the time domain.

■ **underground**

those lines and apparatus below ground, in vaults or manholes, or directly buried in the ground itself.

■ **underground cable**

an insulated cable placed in an underground conduit or direct buried.

■ **undershoot**

transient change in a converter output voltage that does not meet the lower limit of the voltage accuracy specificiation. Typically occurs at converter turn on/off or with some step change in output load or input line. Also see **voltage accuracy.**

■ **undervoltage lockout**

design feature that helps regulate the quality of the output voltage by turning the device OFF in response to supply voltages that fall below its UVLO level. Raychem power switches have a nominal UVLO threshold of 2.5V. Synonyms: UVLO

■ **ungrounded junction**

a form of construction of a thermocouple probe where the hot or measuring junction is fully enclosed by and insulated from the sheath material.

■ **uninterruptible power supply (ups)**

power supply that will continue to operate after the loss of AC input power.

■ **union**

a form of pipe fitting where two extension pipes are joined at a separable coupling.

■ **unipolar**

a signal range that is always positive or always negative, for example 0 to +10 V.

■ **unmodeled dynamics**

dynamics which have not been modeled for any of the following reasons: (i) becuase they are too complex to model, (ii) becuase they are neglible for the physical situation at hand, or (iii) because they are simply unknown to the individual developing the model. In practice, high frequency dynamics are usually not well modeled because of uncertainty associated with them. Such dynamics are therefore sometimes neglected. Control engineers should always strive to quantify how large an error is being made by making such an approximation. They should also understand how the approximation will affect the performance of the final control system design.

■ **unstable system**

usually refers to systems which possess at least one pole in the open right half plane or a double pole at the origin or complex conjugate double poles on the imaginary axis. The first is associated with a rising exponential or a rising exponential sinusoid. The latter two are associated with ramp-like signals in the time domain. Also see **stable system.**

■ **UPS**

(Uninterruptible Power Supply) a power supply which continues to supply power during a loss of input power. Two types are the stand-alone UPS, which is located external to the equipment being powered, and the battery back-up power supply, which is embedded in the equipment being powered, such as a POWER-ONE SPM series high power product with a G5 battery back-up module.

■ **USB**

Universal Serial Bus interoperability standard that defines the electrical power and signal transfer requirements in computing and multi-media applications. USB power requirements define a supply and output voltage of 5V, with output currents rated at 0.5A for self-powered equipment and 0.1A output for bus-powered equipment.

■ **uvlo**

design feature that helps regulate the quality of the output voltage by turning the device OFF in response to supply voltages that fall below its UVLO level. Raychem power switches have a nominal UVLO threshold of 2.5V.

■ **V.C.X.O**

the abbreviation for 'Voltage Controlled Crystal Oscillator.' Such an oscillator contains a network that employs changes in voltage to change the output frequency.

■ **vac**

aC Voltage

■ **vacuum**

any pressure less than atmospheric pressure.

■ **vacuum degassed bearings**

vacuum degassing is a process used in the purifying of steel for ball bearings assuring a very dense and consistent bearing surface. This results in a longer lasting superior bearing. All Reliance Electric ball bearings are vacuum degassed bearings.

■ **vacuum tube**

a form of electron tube in which the envelope contains a vacuum, as opposed to a gas-filled electron tube, in which gases are pumped into the envelope after the air is removed.

■ **variable capacitor**

a capacitor in which the capacitance can be varied by some mechanical means.

■ **variable torque**

a multi-speed motor used on

loads whose torque requirements vary with speed as in some centrifugal pumps and blowers. The HP varies as the square of the speed.

■ **VBSL**

Very High Bit-rate Subscriber Line

■ **velocity**

The time rate of change of displacement; dx/dt.

■ **vertical 'p' base motor**

a vertical motor with a special mounting face conforming to NEMA's 'P' design and with a ring groove on the shaft.

■ **vertical motor**

a motor being mounted vertically (shaft up or down) as in many pump applications.

■ **vibration error**

the maximum change in output of a transducer when a specific amplitude and range of frequencies are applied to a specific axis at room temperature.

■ **vibration error band**

the error recorded in output of a transducer when subjected to a given set of amplitudes and frequencies.

■ **viscosity**

The inherent resistance of a substance to flow.

■ **vmax**

the highest voltage that can safely be dropped across a polyswitch device in its tripped state under specified fault conditions. Synonyms: Maximum Device Voltage, Maximum Interrupt Voltage, Maximum Voltage

■ **volt**

The (electrical) potential difference between two points in a circuit. The fundamental unit is derived as work per unit charge-(V = W/ Q). One volt is the potential difference required to move one coulomb of charge between two points in a circuit while using one joule of energy.

■ **volt amperes**

a unit of apparent power which is the product of electrical pressure x the current.

■ **volt microsecond constant**

the product of the voltage applied across the winding and the time for the magnetising current to reach 1.5 times the linear extrapolation of the current waveform. This constant is a measure of the energy handling capability of a transformer or inductor. It is dependent upon the core area, core material (including the saturation flux density of the core), the number of turns of the winding and tile duty cycle of the applied pulse.

■ **voltage**

the force that causes a current to flow in an electrical circuit. Analogous to pressure in hydraulics, voltage is often referred to as electrical pressure. The voltage of a motor is usually determined by the supply to which it is being attached. NEMA requires that the motor be

able to carry their rated horsepower at nameplate voltage plus
or minus 10% although not necessarily at the rated temperature
rise.

■ **voltage balance**

the difference in magnitudes, in
percent, of two output voltages
that have equal nominal voltage
magnitudes but opposite polarities.

■ **voltage clamping**

the circuitry necessary to protect
relay or solid-state switching elements from excessive voltage. A
possible source of this excessive
voltage could be caused by switching current into inductive loads.

■ **voltage compensation**

voltage compensation reduces
changes in lighting level that occur when air conditioners, refrigerators, and other electrical appliances switch on/off.

■ **voltage discount**

a credit adjustment given to a customer who receives electricity at
primary voltage.

■ **voltage drop**

the loss of voltage between the
input to a device and the output
from a device due to the internal
impedance or resistance of the
device. In all electrical systems, the
conductors should be sized so that
the voltage drop never exceeds 3%
for power, heating, and lighting
loads or combinations of these.
furthermore, the maximum total
voltage drop for conductors for
feeders and branch circuits combined should never exceed 5%.

■ **voltage mode**

a method of closed loop control
of a switching converter where the
pulse width is varied in response
to changes in the output voltage
to regulate the output.

■ **voltage, maximum**

the highest voltage that can safely
be dropped across a polyswitch
device in its tripped state under
specified fault conditions. Synonyms: Maximum Device Voltage,
Maximum Interrupt Voltage,
Vmax

■ **voltage, maximum operating**

the maximum voltage across a
polyswitch device under a typical
fault condition. In many circuits,
this is the voltage of the power
source in the circuit. It may be
possible to use a polyswitch device
at a higher voltage, but each such
use must be individually qualified.

■ **voltage-to-frequency
converter**

a device that converts an analogue
input voltage into a sequence of
digital pulses with a frequency that
is proportional to the input voltage.

■ **volt-ampere**

in an a.c. circuit, a measure of
apparent power, given by: VA-EI,
where E is the potential in volts; I
is the current in amperes; and VA
is apparent power in volt-amperes

■ **voltmeter**

an instrument used to measure
voltage.

volt-microsecond constant

the product of the voltage applied across the winding and the time for the magnetising current to reach 1.5 times the linear extrapolation of the current waveform. This constant is a measure of the energy handling capability of a transformer or inductor. It is dependent upon the core area, core material, number of turns, and the duty cycle of the applied pulse.

volts

a flow of electric charge.

volume flow rate

calculated using the area of the full closed conduit and the average fluid velocity in the form, $Q = V \times A$, to arrive at the total volume quantity of flow. Q = volumetric flowrate, V = average fluid velocity, and A = cross sectional area of the pipe.

volume resistivilty (core)

the ability of a core to resist the flow of electrical current either through the bulk of the material or on its surface. The unit of the volume resistivity is Ohm-cm. Core volume resistivity becomes an issue in inductor designs where the leads/terminals come in contact with the core material. This type includes axial and radial inductors that have leads epoxied into the core. As for core materials, high permeability ferrites present the most concern as their volume resistivity is typically the lowest. Under certain conditions, a low resistive path can be realized between two inductor terminals if they are in contact with a low resistivity core. The inductor, under these conditions, will lose its higher impedance characteristics.

VPN

Virtual Private Network

VSWR

abbreviation for Voltage Standing Wave Ratio. The loss due to the mismatch introduced into the signal by the load or source signal path characteristics. Expressed as a ratio of the highest voltage to the lowest voltage found in the signal. Also expressed as Return Loss in dB. The Return Loss expression is the more modern term.

VSWR (voltage standing wave ratio)

amount of reflected power expressed as a ratio VSWR increases as frequency increases.

vt 154

an instrument which indicates approximate voltage.

vxi

a newer electrical and mechanical standard (based on the VME standard, with Extensions for Instrumentation) mainly utilised in the ATE industry to assist different vendor's equipment to work together in a common control and packaging environment.

■ **wallbox dimmer**

a self-contained dimmer that fits into a wallbox.

■ **WAN**

wide Area Network- A network which encompasses interconnectivity between devices over a wide geographic area.

■ **warm-up drift**

the initial change in the output voltage of a power supply in the time period between turn-on and when the power supply reaches thermal equilibrium at 25 degrees Centigrade, full load and nominal line.

■ **warmup time**

time required for a converter to operate within specifications after turn-on. This time normally precedes a long-term drift specification.

■ **watertight**

so constructed that water/moisture will not enter the enclosure under specified test conditions.

■ **watt**

a unit of power defined as a joule of energy per second. Named in honor of James Watt who in 1765 constructed the first practical steam engine, originally used to power mechanical pumps to remove water from coal mines (see joules).

■ **watt**

unit of electrical power required to do work at the rate of one joule per second. One watt of power is expended when one ampere of direct current flows through a resistance of one ohm. In an AC circuit, true power is the product of effective volts and effective amperes, multiplied by the power factor.

■ **watt density**

the watts emanating from each square inch of heated surface area of a heater. Expressed in units of watts per square inch.

■ **wattage rating**

maximum power a device can safely handle continously.

■ **watt-hour**

unit of electrical work, equal to a power of one watt being absorbed for one hour.

■ **watt-hour meter**

an instrument that records the power used in watt-hours.

■ **wattmeter**

instrument used to measure electric power in watts.

■ **wave**

electric, electromagnetic, acoustic, mechanical or other form whose physical activity rises and falls or advances and retreats periodically as it travels through some medium.

■ **waveform**

shape of a wave.

■ **waveguide**

rectangular or circular pipe used to guide electromagnetic waves at microfrequencies.

wavelength

distance between two points of corresponding phase and is equal to waveform velocity divided by frequency.

WBI

Web-Based Intranets

weatherhead

the point of entrance to service conduit from service drop. A device to keep water from entering service conduit.

weatherproof

so constructed or protected that exposure to the weather will not interfere with successful operation.

weather-protected machine Type I

(WPI) weather-protected machine is an open machine with its ventilating passages so constructed as to minimize the entrance of rain, snow and airborne particles to the electric parts and having its ventilating openings so constructed as to prevent the passage of a cylindrical rod 3/4 inch in diameter.

weather-protected machine Type II

(WPII) shall have, in addition to the enclosure defined for a Type 1 weather-protected machine, its ventilating passages at both intake and discharge so arranged that high velocity air and airborne particles blown into the machine by storms or high winds can be discharged without entering the internal ventilating passages leading directly to the electric parts of the machine itself. The normal path of the ventilating air which enters the electric parts of the machines shall be so arranged by baffling or separate housing as to provide at least three abrupt changes in direction, none of which shall be less than $90f$. In addition, an area of low velocity not exceeding 600 feet per minute shall be provided in the intake air path to minimize the possibility of moisture or dirt being carried into the electric parts of the machine.

weber

(Wb) Standard unit of magnetic flux measurement equal to 100,000,000, or 10 to the 8th power lines of force. The previously used unit of magnetic flux was the Maxwell, which was equal to one magnetic line of force.

wet cell

secondary cell using a liquid as an electrolyte.

wetting

term used in soldering to describe the condition that occurs when the metals being soldered are hot enough to melt the solder so it flows over the surface.

wheatstone bridge

a network of four resistances, an emf source, and a galvanometer connected such that when the four resistances are matched, the galvanometer will show a zero deflection or 'null' reading.

wholesale consumer

any entity that purchases electricity at the wholesale level, including municipal utilities, private utilities, rural electric cooperatives, or government-owned utility districts. Wholesale consumers purchase electricity from other wholesale suppliers to resell to their own retail consumers.

■ **wholesale wheeling**

the process of sending electricity from one utility to another wholesale purchaser over the transmission lines of an intermediate utility. Under the Energy Policy Act of 1992, utilities are required to provide wholesale transmission wheeling services to any electric utility, federal power marketing agency, or other company generating electric energy for sale in the wholesale market

■ **wide area network (WAN)**

a network that spans a greater distance and needs the involvement of a public carrier.

■ **wideband**

1) an adjective describing the characteristics of a communications circuit or channel that can carry a large quantity of information at a high rate. 2) In video applications, a circuit or system with sufficient bandwidth to convey very high resolution information in an image (video) signal. For reconstructed video images from a computer, the required bandwidth is half the pixel clock rate.

■ **wideband amplifier**

also called 'broadband amplifier.' Amplifier with a flat response over a wide range of frequencies.

■ **wien-bridge oscillator**

oscillator that uses an RC low-pass filter and an RC high-pass filter to set the frequncy of oscillations.

■ **wind energy**

refers to the kinetic (in motion) energy of the wind which can turn a wind turbine and this generates electricity.

■ **wind turbine**

windmill of advanced aerodynamic design connected to an electricity generator and used in windpower installations. Wind turbines can be either large propeller-type rotors mounted on a tall tower, or flexible metal strips fixed to a vertical axle at top and bottom.

■ **winding**

one or more turns of a conductor wound in the form of a coil.

■ **winding factor (k)**

the ratio of the total area of copper wire inside the centre hole of a toroid to the window area of the toroid.

■ **window**

in computer graphics, a defined area in a system not bounded by any limits; unlimited 'space' in graphics.

■ **window area (wa)**

the area in and around a magnetic core which can be used for the placement of windings.

wire

single solid or stranded group of conductors having a low resistance to current flow. Used to make connections between circuits or points in a circuit.

wire gauge

american wire gauge (AWG) is a system of numerical designations of wire diameters.

wire wrapping

method of making a connection by wrapping wire around a rectangular pin.

wireless

term describing radio communication that requires no wired between two communicating points.

wirewound resistor

resistor in which the resistive element is a length of high resistance wire or ribbon usually nichrome wound onto an insulating form.

withstand voltage

maximum voltage level that can be applied between circuits or components without causing a breakdown. Also see **breakdown voltage and isolation.**

Wk2 (moment of inertia)

the moment of inertia is expressed as Wk^2 or WR^2 in terms of pound-feet squared. It is the product of the weight of the object in pounds and the square of the radius of gyration in feet. If the application is such that the motor is driving through a pulley or gear so that the driven equipment is operating at a higher or lower speed than the motor, it is necessary to calculate the inertia 'reflected to the motor shaft,' that is, an equivalent Wk^2(reflected to motor shaft) = Wk^2 based on the rpm of the motor. Wk^2(reflected to motor shaft) = Wk^2(driven equipment) x

WLL

Wireless Local Loop

woofer

large loudspeaker designed primarily to reproduce low frequency audio signals.

word

Number of bits treated as a single unit by the CPU. In an 8-bit machine, the word length is 8 bits; in a sixteen bit machine, it is 16 bits.

work

in physics, a measure of the result of transferring energy from one system to another to cause an object to move. Work should not be confused with energy (the capacity to do work, which is also measured in joules) or with power (the rate of doing work, measured in joules per second).

work area

building space where occupants utilise telecommunications equipment.

working standard

a standard of unit measurement calibrated from either a primary or secondary standard which is used to calibrate other devices or make comparison measurements.

■ **wound rotor induction motor**

a wound rotor induction motor is an induction motor in which the secondary circuit consists of polyphase winding or coils whose terminals are either short circuited or closed through suitable circuits. A wound rotor motor is sometimes used when high breakdown torque and a soft start or variable speed are required.

■ **write**

To record data in a storage device or on a data medium.

■ **wye system**

a method of connecting three single transformers for three-phase application.

■ **wye-delta starting**

a method of starting a motor at rated voltage but drawing locked rotor current and producing reduced stocked rotor torque but it provides lower starting torque than a straight delta connection. Once the load and motor have been started the wiring will switch from the wye connection to a delta connection in which mode it must run and deliver full torque.

■ **x**

symbol for reactance.

■ **x-axis**

conventionally, the horizontal axis of any type of graph.

■ **xdsl**

refers to the various flavours of DSL (Digital Subscriber Loop). All

encompassing term.

■ **XML**

Extensible Markup Language

■ **y**

symbol for admittance.

■ **y-axis**

conventionally, the axis perpendicular to and in the horizontal plane through the x-axis of any type of graph.

■ **youla parameterisation**

parameterisations which parameterises the set of all stabilising controllers for an LTI plant.

■ **Young's modulus**

Young's Modulus (the Modulus of Elasticity) is equivalent to the ratio of normal stress to strain.

■ **z-axis**

conventionally, the vertical axis in any three-dimensional co-ordinate system.

■ **zener diode**

a diode that maintains a relatively constant voltage when the reverse voltage across it is increased passed a specific point, called the zener voltage.

■ **zero**

refers to input frequencies which are absorbed by a system.

■ **zero adjustment**

the ability to adjust the display of a process or strain meter so that zero on the display corresponds to a non-zero signal, such as 4 mA, 10 mA, or 1 V dc. The adjustment range is normally expressed in counts.

zero balance

with transducers like strain gauges, the output is large compared to the changes caused by the strain. Setting a zero balance subtracts an offset (actually a fraction of the bridge excitation voltage), so the changes caused by the strain can be accurately measured.

zero input response

response of a system with the input set to zero; response to an inital condition with no input.

zero offset

the difference expressed in degrees between true zero and an indication given by a measuring instrument.

zero point

the electrical zero point where zero millivolts would be displayed. Used in conjunction with the slope control to provide a narrower range calibration.

zero power resistance

the resistance of a thermistor or RTD element with no power being dissipated.

zero state response

response of a system with the state set to zero; response to an input with zero initial condition.

zero suppression

the span of an indicator or chart recorder may be offset from zero (zero suppressed) such that neither limit of the span will be zero. For example, a temperature recorder which records a 100° span from 400° to 500° is said to have 400° zero suppression.

zero voltage switching

the making or breaking of circuit timed such that the transition occurs when the voltage wave form crosses zero voltage; typically only found in solid state switching devices.

zeroing

calibrating a meter so that it shows a value of zero when zero is being measured.

zeta

greek letter used to denote damping ratio or damping factor. Also see **underdamped poles**.

zone

a fixture or group of fixtures controlled simultaneously as a single entity.

zooming

in computer graphics, causing an object to appear smaller or larger by moving the window and specifying various window sizes.

Notes

Notes

Notes

Notes